Quiz Yourself!

1800 Questions and Answers

David Self

Ward Lock Educational

ISBN 0 7062 4157 6

First published in 1982
by Ward Lock Educational
47 Marylebone Lane, London W1M 6AX
A Ling Kee company

Set in 11 on 13 point Times Roman
by Ilford Photosetting Company, Essex IG3 8EE
and printed by Chigwell Press, Buckhurst Hill, Essex

Contents

Introduction
The Quizzes

The Answers

Introduction

This is a bumper book of quizzes for all occasions. It can provide plenty of fun for the whole family, amongst friends, as a basis for school or group contests, or when you just want to test your knowledge.

The one hundred quizzes in this book include many general knowledge quizzes, and also more specialized quizzes covering everything from films to food, and from spelling to sport. You will find the answers to the quizzes at the back of the book. This means that you can refer to them easily, but you can also avoid any temptation to cheat! There is space on each page, which you can use either for filling in the answers or for keeping the scores — and if you do this lightly in pencil, you can use the book again and again.

There are many ways to run a quiz. You can divide into two or more teams, or individuals can compete against each other. There must of course be an impartial quiz-master or -mistress, to ask the questions and keep the scores. You should not need an adjudicator, because the questions are deliberately straightforward, the answers short and to the point, and any alternative answers are supplied; but you may need a scorer, or someone to check the quiz-master or -mistress's scoring.

How you score is again up to you. You may want to award two points for a correct answer, one point for a 'half-correct' answer, one point for a corrected answer from the opposing team if a question is passed over, and nothing for a wrong answer. Or you may like to give a sequence of, say, six questions to one team (or person), and then to award a bonus for getting them all right.

To make a quiz more exciting, you can bring in a timing element, and impose time limits for individual questions or sequences of questions. You can add variety by letting your teams confer in some rounds but not in others.

And, finally, you can make up other kinds of rounds to go with the quizzes here. You can show slides, photographs, or newspaper cuttings, for example of famous landmarks, famous people, or important recent or current events; you can play brief excerpts from records, or a pianist can play snatches of tunes; you can invent questions about current pop groups, radio and television series, or local personalities; and you can look at current events. And if you look closely at the questions in this book, you will not only have the material for one hundred ready-made quizzes but also the ideas for many, many more.

Quiz No. 1 General Knowledge 1

1. What is the tide doing when it is ebbing?

2. What is a red-letter day?

3. What kind of animal is a Borzoi?

4. Who was Guinevere's husband?

5. In America, what is meant by a capital S with one or two vertical lines drawn through it? ($)

6. In a song, whom did a jolly swagman want to come dancing with him?

7. Not counting Australia, which is the world's largest island?

8. Of which country is Baffin Island a part?

9. In which ocean are the Azores?

10. To which country does the island of Corfu belong?

11. On which island was Napoleon born?

12. On which island did Napoleon die?

13. Where would you find treads and risers close together?

14. In radio and television, for what do the initials BBC stand?

15. From which country would porcelain of the Ming dynasty come?

16. What is pumpernickel?

17. Which ancient Mexican people were overthrown by Cortez?

18. According to the Bible, what shall the meek inherit?

Quiz No. 2   **Abbreviations**

1. Which organization is represented by the letters UN?

2. For what do the letters VIP stand?

3. What do the initials RSVP on an invitation mean?

4. Which medal is represented by the letters VC?

5. Three letters are often used as a distress signal. What are they?

6. For what do the letters OHMS stand?

7. For what does the abbreviation 'anon' stand?

8. For what word is 'pram' an abbreviation?

9. Russia is also known as the USSR. What do these letters stand for?

10. If you saw the letters PTO at the bottom of a page, what would they mean?

11. If a parcel arrives COD, what does COD mean?

12. In America, for what do the initials CIA stand?

13. In transport, for what do the letters HGV stand?

14. For what do the letters SEATO stand?

15. For what do the letters EEC stand?

16. For what do the initials NATO stand?

17. For what do the initials ETA stand?

18. With which army do you associate the abbreviation SPQR?

Quiz No. 3   **Aviation**

1. Of which country is Aer Lingus the national airline?

2. Of which country is Lufthansa the national airline?

3. Of which country is Sabena the national airline?

4. Of which country is Quantas an airline?

5. Of which country is KLM the national airline?

6. By what nickname is a Boeing 747 generally known?

7. What information does a pilot get from his altimeter?

8. For which city is 'Charles de Gaulle' an airport?

9. For which city is 'Leonardo da Vinci' an airport?

10. If you landed at Heathrow Airport, into which city would you be going?

11. If you landed at La Guardia airport, in which city would you be?

12. Which two countries worked together to develop the Concorde aircraft?

13. Who was the famous woman aviator who flew from England to Australia in 1930?

14. Who were the first two men to fly the Atlantic non-stop?

15. Who flew in the famous aircraft, 'Spirit of St Louis'?

16. Who was the first man to fly the Channel by aeroplane?

17. Which aircraft made a round-the-world flight in 1929?

18. In 1930 a famous British airship was destroyed in France on its first flight to India. What was it known as?

Quiz No. 4   General Knowledge 2

1. Are sponges animal, vegetable or mineral?

2. What do you do if you keep vigil?

3. What is a tarn?

4. In which country would you find Lake Lucerne?

5. In which industry would you work if you won an Oscar?

6. Which king led the Saxons at the Battle of Hastings?

7. In which European capital city would you find the Coliseum?

8. In which city would you be if you were walking along the Champs Elysées?

9. Is the Horn of Africa in the north, south, east or west of the continent?

10. What does the Latin word *Salve* mean?

11. Which famous general was killed at Khartoum in 1885?

12. What is bullion?

13. What was Iran formerly called?

14. What was Thailand formerly called?

15. Which country was once known as Albion?

16. What was Sri Lanka formerly called?

17. What is the modern equivalent for the old-fashioned name 'Hibernia'?

18. What is the modern equivalent for the old-fashioned name 'Cathay'?

Quiz No. 5   Family Matters

1. How long have you been married if you are celebrating your silver wedding anniversary?

2. How long have you been married if you are celebrating your golden wedding anniversary?

3. Who is your maternal grandmother?

4. Who is your paternal grandfather?

5. How old is a centenarian?

6. What is a widow?

7. Is your fraternal relative your brother, uncle or father?

8. What relation to you is your avuncular relative?

9. If all your great grandparents were alive, how many would you have?

10. Many Scottish surnames begin with 'Mac'. What does 'Mac' mean?

11. For what first name is Nessy often an abbreviation?

12. For what first name is Sadie often an abbreviation?

13. Spell the girl's name Frances.

14. Which sign of the Zodiac is known as the twins?

15. What precious stone denotes your 40th wedding anniversary?

16. What is your 60th wedding anniversary called?

17. How old is an nonogenarian?

18. In Greek mythology who was supposed to have killed his father and married his mother?

Quiz No. 6   Birds

1. Do penguins live in the Arctic or Antarctic?

2. Which large bird is said to bury its head in the sand when it's afraid?

3. Which bird is famous for laying its eggs in other birds' nests?

4. Which bird is a symbol of wisdom?

5. In what formation do migrating geese often fly?

6. What is the name given to a place in which birds are kept?

7. What do we call the study of birds?

8. With which bird is the island of Lundy traditionally associated?

9. In which country are kiwis found?

10. Brent, Grey-lag and Pink Footed are all types of what?

11. Whooper, Bewick and Mute are all types of which bird?

12. What sort of bird is a Cinnamon Norwich?

13. What kind of bird is a cockatoo?

14. Which bird is often used as a symbol of peace?

15. Which bird supposedly sings, 'A little bit of bread and no cheese'?

16. Which bird has the greatest wing span?

17. Which is the largest bird in the world?

18. Which bird is sometimes shown as a symbol of the United States of America?

Quiz No. 7   General Knowledge 3

1. Which animal is said to go mad in March?

2. What is a book worm?

3. Which vitamin is plentiful in oranges and lemons?

4. What kind of transport is a 'whirlybird'?

5. Georgia, Latvia and Estonia are now all part of which country?

6. What is the capital of Brazil?

Fruits
7. What are Golden Delicious, Granny Smiths and Codlings?

8. Which fruit did Eve eat in the Garden of Eden?

9. Name two citrus fruits.

10. What are fruits de mer?

11. Which fruit is a cross between a blackberry and a raspberry?

12. What kind of fruit did Persephone eat during her stay in Hades?

13. What is the light sealskin-covered boat used by Eskimos?

14. In the modern three-core electric cable, which colour wire is connected to neutral?

15. Which emperor supposedly fiddled while Rome burned?

16. What is a 'sackbut'?

17. What kind of meat is properly used to make Wiener Schnitzel?

18. Which composer is famous for his 'Rhapsody in Blue'?

Quiz No. 8   Buildings

1. What do we call a building where flour is made?

2. What do we call a building where beer is made?

3. What do we call a factory in which oil is processed?

4. What do we usually call the strip of water that surrounds a medieval castle?

5. What is a dormer window?

6. What part of a building is the façade?

7. What are dried in an oast house?

8. Where on a wall are coping tiles or stones?

9. Where in a building would you see a lintel?

10. Where in a church would you find a crypt?

11. On what type of building would you be most likely to see crenellation?

12. For what purpose did the Ancient Egyptians build the Pyramids?

13. What do we call a place where leather is prepared?

14. What was a catacomb?

15. A mullion is a part of what?

16. Where would you usually find a lych-gate?

17. In what sort of building would you be most likely to find a portcullis?

18. What do we call a building where whisky is made?

Quiz No. 9   Films

1. In the Tom and Jerry cartoons, which is the mouse?

2. What vegetable does the cartoon character, Popeye, eat to make himself strong?

3. Who is Batman's assistant?

4. What kind of monster is King Kong?

5. Who was Oliver Hardy's partner?

6. Who created the film character Donald Duck?

7. In the Walt Disney film title, how many dalmations were there?

8. In which film would you see CP30 and R2D2?

9. What number is especially associated with James Bond?

10. For which film role is Johnny Weismuller chiefly remembered?

11. What is the name of the cartoon cat that never quite manages to catch Tweetie Pie?

12. Name four of the seven dwarfs in *Snow White*?

13. The film *Tora! Tora! Tora!* was about a Japanese attack on which American base?

14. Name the two men who star in the film *Butch Cassidy and the Sundance Kid?*

15. What was the name of the 'crazy cops' created by the film producer, Mack Sennett?

16. Who was the star of the first successful talking feature film?

17. Who played the female lead in the film version of *The Sound of Music?*

18. In the Pink Panther films, who plays Inspector Clouseau?

Quiz No. 10   General Knowledge 4

Clock times

1. What time is 19.00 hours?

2. What time is 22.00 hours?

3. What time is 21.15 hours?

4. What time of day is 20.00 hours?

5. What time of day is 23.45?

6. What time is 17.30?

_____

7. What is meant by walking in 'Indian' file?

8. Which month is named after the Roman god of war?

9. In 1875, Captain Matthew Webb was the first man to do what?

10. If an American said he had a flat, what would he mean?

11. Who are your 'kith and kin'?

12. In which town or village did Jesus turn water into wine?

13. In which country is Mount Fuji situated?

14. How many angles has a decagon?

15. With which means of transport is IATA concerned?

16. Who was the first king to rule over both England and Scotland?

17. In which Shakespeare play do we meet a monster called Caliban?

18. What is a 'fob'?

Quiz No. 11   America

1. In the Wild West, for what was Annie Oakley famous?

2. Which American folk-hero was 'King of the Wild Frontier'?

3. In which American state is the city of Dallas?

4. In which American state is the city of Memphis?

5. What does an American mean by gasoline?

6. Which season of the year is known in America as the Fall?

7. Name the two main political parties in the USA.

8. What is the statue at the entrance of New York harbour called?

9. Which American president was assassinated in a theatre?

10. In which American war was the Battle of Gettysburg?

11. In which American state is Long Beach?

12. In which city is there a district known as The Bronx?

13. Which American president had the first names Richard Milhous?

14. Which American state was founded by the Quaker William Penn in 1682?

15. Franklin D. Roosevelt — for what did the 'D' stand?

16. Dwight D. Eisenhower — for what did the 'D' stand?

17. In area, which is the largest of the United States of America?

18. Which American state is sometimes nicknamed the Lone Star State?

Quiz No. 12 Food 1

1. Cheddar, Brie, Edam and cottage are all kinds of what food?

2. Which meat is traditionally eaten at Christmas?

3. Besides batter, what must you have to make a toad-in-the-hole?

4. What do the English call an egg-plant?

5. What traditional Scottish food is a meaty pudding cooked inside a sheep's stomach?

6. Is tapioca animal, vegetable or mineral?

7. Why is yeast added to bread dough?

8. From which part of an egg do we make meringues?

9. What is paprika?

10. What is the principal ingredient of cole slaw?

11. What is the main ingredient in a syllabub?

12. On which day of the year in particular do we eat hot-cross buns?

13. On a menu, what is meant by 'petits pois'?

14. If you were in a restaurant and ordered 'pommes de terres frites' what would you get?

15. What kind of food is a saveloy?

16. From which part of a cow do we get tripe?

17. Of which country is paella a national dish?

18. From which country does mousaka come?

Quiz No. 13   General Knowledge 5

1. How many letters are there in the English alphabet?

2. In our alphabet, which letter comes immediately before Q?

3. Who heard bells telling him to turn again?

4. How many days are there in the month of February during a leap year?

5. In land area, which is the largest continent?

6. The Roman numeral L represents which number?

7. What do we call a baby kangaroo?

8. What do we call a female pig?

9. Besides a dog, who would wear a dog collar?

10. Which people traditionally wear kilts?

11. In which city will you find the Kremlin?

12. In which Italian city would you find a leaning tower?

13. What do these have in common,— Mount St. Helens, Vesuvius, Etna?

14. What do these have in common — reef, half-hitch, sheepshank?

15. What name is given to fermented apple juice?

16. If offered a choice of Indian or China, what would you be about to drink?

17. What terrible disaster struck London in 1665?

18. In which year did the English defeat the Spanish Armada?

Quiz No. 14   Animals

1. How does a kangaroo carry its young?

2. What is the main feature by which you would recognize a zebra?

3. How would you recognize a Manx cat?

4. Which animal's tail is often called a brush?

5. In which position does a sloth often hang?

6. What happens when an animal or bird 'moults'?

7. When a horse stands up, which legs does it get up on first?

8. What was the name of Alexander the Great's famous horse?

9. Which is the tallest existing mammal?

10. Over a short distance, which is generally said to be the fastest land animal?

11. In which country would you be most likely to find a wallaby in the wild?

12. What is a 'nocturnal' animal?

13. Which animal is suggested by the word 'porcine'?

14. With which animal do you associate the word 'feline'?

15. Blue, bottle-nosed and humpback are all types of which animal?

16. Abyssinian, Chinchilla, Tortoiseshell are all breeds of what sort of animal?

17. Nowadays, which is the largest land animal in the world?

18. In the animal kingdom, what are amphibians?

Quiz No. 15   Games 1

1. For which of these games would you use a dice: ludo, whist, hopscotch, snakes-and-ladders?

2. Which game used to be known as ping-pong?

3. Where can you see knights, bishops and castles very close together?

4. What is the usual number of pins in a game of skittles?

5. In which country is Gaelic Football chiefly played?

6. In which game do you use a shuttlecock?

7. At the start of a game, how many pawns are there on a chess board?

8. In which game does the term 'cannon' occur?

9. Which game is also known as Checkers?

10. In golf, what is a 'birdie'?

11. In chess, what is another name for a 'rook'?

12. Not counting jokers, how many playing cards are there in a standard pack?

13. Which popular American game developed from the English game rounders?

14. On a dartboard, what score is the innermost ring?

15. How many pieces are there in a standard set of dominoes?

16. In which card game might you hold a 'full house'?

17. At the beginning of a game of snooker, how many red balls are on the table?

18. With what do you play cribbage?

Quiz No. 16   General Knowledge 6

1. What are humbugs, gobstoppers and dolly mixtures?

2. Which country is famous for its Eisteddfod?

3. What would you keep in a menagerie?

4. How would you recognize a Bactrian camel?

5. Which courtier is supposed to have laid his cloak over a puddle so that Queen Elizabeth I could keep her feet dry?

6. What do you do if you 'boycott' something?

7. How many arms does an octopus have?

8. In our alphabet, which letter comes next but one after F?

9. Which letter of the alphabet is used to describe a hard lead pencil?

10. Which letter of the alphabet is used to describe a soft lead pencil?

11. What is the first letter of the Greek alphabet?

12. What is the last letter of the Greek alphabet?

13. In which war was the Siege of Mafeking?

14. Who wrote *Animal Farm?*

15. In 1498, who painted 'The Last Supper'?

16. What is lapis lazuli?

17. Which part of the American continent was explored by John Cabot?

18. How many colours are there in the spectrum?

Quiz No. 17   Art

1. Which Dutch painter cut off one of his own ears?

2. Which painter had a 'blue period'?

3. Origami is the Japanese art of what?

4. There is a famous painting of some sunflowers. Was it painted by Picasso, Renoir or van Gogh?

5. The artist Frans Hals painted a famous cavalier. What was the cavalier doing?

6. Which artist painted the picture 'Whistler's Mother'?

7. Which portrait by Leonardo da Vinci is famous for its smile?

8. Which famous French artist painted a picture called 'At the Moulin-Rouge'?

9. Who painted the picture 'The Blue Boy'?

10. Who painted the picture 'The Fighting Temeraire'?

11. Which English painter is famous for his picture 'The Cornfield'?

12. Which famous painter decorated the ceiling of the Sistine Chapel?

13. What nationality was the painter Picasso?

14. Which French artist is famous for painting ballet dancers?

15. On what would a fresco be painted?

16. Which painter also invented a type of helicopter and a parachute?

17. In painting, what are the three primary colours?

18. George Stubbs was famous for painting which animal?

Quiz No. 18   Composers

1. Who composed the famous 'Moonlight Sonata'?

2. Who wrote the 'Blue Danube' waltz?

3. Who composed the '1812' Overture?

4. Which composer wrote the 'Water Music'?

5. What was the surname of the composer whose first names were Wolfgang Amadeus?

6. What was the surname of the composer whose first names were Johann Sebastian?

7. Which famous composer went on composing after he had gone deaf?

8. Which famous composer left a symphony unfinished in 1822?

9. Who composed the 'Hallelujah Chorus'?

10. Who composed the 'Nutcracker' ballet suite?

11. What nationality was the composer Elgar?

12. Which was Chopin's country of birth?

13. Who composed 'Eine Kleine Nacht Musik'?

14. Which composer wrote 'The Flight of the Bumble Bee'?

15. Who composed 'Finlandia'?

16. Whose Symphony No. 94 is known as the Surprise Symphony?

17. Who composed the Eroica and Pastoral symphonies?

18. Who composed the Brandenburg Concertos?

Quiz No. 19   General Knowledge 7

1. In which activity are 'yoicks' and 'tally ho' traditionally shouted?

2. Traditionally, which group of men used to dance the hornpipe?

3. Who uses a hod?

4. What was the middle name of the Danish writer Hans Andersen?

5. What is special about a deciduous tree?

6. What colour is the flag of the Republic of Ireland?

7. What pet animal did organ grinders often used to have?

8. You probably know what a fan club is; what is the word 'fan' short for?

9. Who was the Roman goddess of love?

10. What was the name of the Greek goddess of love?

11. What is the opposite of occidental?

12. A biography and an autobiography are both life stories. What is the difference?

13. On what does a 'carnivore' feed?

14. What crime do you commit if you betray your country?

15. What crime do you commit if you marry more than one person at once?

16. To what might someone add a codicil?

17. If you have committed patricide, what have you done?

18. If you have committed regicide, what have you done?

Quiz No. 20   Associations

1. With what is Fleet Street in London associated?

2. With what is Broadway in New York associated?

3. With what is Hollywood in California associated?

4. With which precious stone do we associate Amsterdam?

5. With which ceremony do we associate orange blossom?

6. With which festival do we associate mistletoe?

   With what do you associate the following famous people:

7. Rudolph Nureyev?

8. Sebastian Coe?

9. Paul Gaugin?

10. Joan Sutherland?

11. Yehudi Menuhin?

12. George Eliot?

13. Can you complete this: 'pestle and ....'?

14. Can you complete this: 'flotsam and ....'?

15. Which dancing partner is associated with Ginger Rogers?

16. 'Dr Jekyll and Mr Hyde' – of these two, which was the unpleasant character?

17. Complete the title of Tolstoy's famous novel: *War and ....*

18. Complete the title of D. H. Lawrence's famous novel: *Sons and ....*

Quiz No. 21   Clothes 1

1. Which people originally wore moccasins?

2. Who is likely to wear a sporran?

3. What is a deer-stalker?

4. What is a cassock?

5. What kind of clothing is a 'stetson'?

6. On which part of the body would a tiara be worn?

7. On which part of the body would an epaulette be worn?

8. Whereabouts would you wear a cummerbund?

9. What is the name of the long robe or dress traditionally worn by Japanese women?

10. What is a yashmak?

11. What head covering is worn by a bishop?

12. What is a parka?

13. Which commander in the Crimean War gave his name to a woollen waistcoat?

14. Which British general has given his name to waterproof footwear?

15. Who would be most likely to wear a tutu?

16. Which film star gave her name to a life jacket?

17. Of what are greaves, gauntlets and a visor all part?

18. What was a doublet?

Quiz No. 22   General Knowledge 8

1. What is the fruit of an oak tree called?

2. Which Roman numerals represent the number 20?

3. What is the common name for the fruit of the vine?

4. For which fruit is Seville famous?

5. Which fruit is dried to make prunes?

6. What kind of fruit did the wicked queen use to poison Snow White?

7. On which river does Vienna stand?

8. What would you see in a planetarium?

9. A book about the Trapp Family was made into a film musical. What was the film called?

10. What is the name of the tiny principality situated between Switzerland and Austria?

11. What is a hurdy gurdy?

12. Which animal is famous for *not being able* to change its spots?

13. What name is given to someone who comes from the Scilly Isles?

14. How many sides has a hexagon?

15. Which black and white bird has a reputation for stealing?

16. For what is Axminster in Devon famous?

17. The followers of Islam are known as what?

18. What invention by Percy Shaw in 1934 has been a great help to motorists?

Quiz No. 23   Authors

1. For which series of children's books is Richmal Crompton famous?

2. Which woman writer wrote a series of books about the Famous Five?

3. Who wrote *The Tale of Peter Rabbit*?

4. Who wrote the book *Chitty Chitty Bang Bang*?

5. Which writer created the character Biggles?

6. Which American writer created Tarzan?

7. Which writer created Midshipman Horatio Hornblower?

8. Who wrote the novel *The Thirty-Nine Steps*?

9. Who wrote the book *Three Men in a Boat*?

10. For what kind of books was Zane Grey famous?

11. Which writer created the detective Hercule Poirot?

12. Which crime writer created the private eye Philip Marlowe?

13. What was the surname of the writer whose first names were William Makepeace?

14. What were the first names of the three Brontë sisters?

15. Who wrote *Nicholas Nickleby*?

16. Who wrote the famous novel *Emma*?

17. Who wrote *Das Kapital*?

18. Who wrote *Pilgrim's Progress*?

Quiz No. 24　On Holiday

1. What is a 'motel'?

2. For which city is Le Bourget an airport?

3. If you wanted to see the Acropolis, to which city would you go?

4. What could you do if you were bilingual?

5. In which park is London Zoo?

6. If you drove west from Switzerland, which country would you enter next?

7. In which cuntry is the holiday resort of Dubrovnik?

8. In which country is the holiday resort of Torremolinos?

9. On which island is the holiday resort of Palma?

10. In which country is the holiday resort of Tangier?

11. In which country is the holiday resort of Estoril?

12. In which country is the holiday resort of Sorrento?

13. In which ocean would you find the Seychelles?

14. If you wanted to visit the famous La Scala opera house, which country would you go to?

15. In which country is Ayer's Rock?

16. From which Paris station would you leave if you were travelling to England via Calais?

17. In France, what is SNCF?

18. For what is the Bordeaux region of France famous?

Quiz No. 25 General Knowledge 9

1. What or who is a spinster?

2. Where would you expect to see a ring-master at work?

3. From which animal do we get venison?

4. Where does a purser normally work?

5. In which country is Havana?

6. Do Christmas and New Year ever occur in the same year?

Flags
7. How many flags are used in semaphore?

8. Which flag was made by combining the crosses of St Andrew, St Patrick and St George?

9. What does a flag at half mast signify?

10. Which country has a Union Jack and four stars of the Southern Cross in red on its flag?

11. What do the stars on the American flag represent?

12. What musical instrument is on the British Royal Standard?

13. For what achievement is Valentina Tereshkova famous?

14. Molars, incisors and canines are all types of what?

15. Whereabouts on a whale are its flukes?

16. Where in the world does the wind blow only from the north?

17. Name two of the Marx Brothers comedy team.

18. Who made a famous 'last stand' at Little Big Horn in 1876?

Quiz No. 26   The Old Testament

1. What is the name of the first man mentioned in the Bible?

2. Who was the giant killed by the boy David?

3. Whom did God tell to build an ark?

4. Who was thrown into a den of lions?

5. What was the name of the Garden where Adam and Eve were tempted?

6. Who wore a coat of many colours?

7. Which man led the Israelites out of Egypt?

8. With which musical instrument is David associated?

9. Who was betrayed by Delilah?

10. On which mountain was Moses given the Ten Commandments?

11. Who pulled down a temple, and in doing so killed himself and also many Philistines?

12. What did Joseph have put in Benjamin's sack?

13. What sign did God give Noah that the earth would not be flooded again?

14. Which kind of bird was the first to leave the Ark?

15. How many human beings were there in the Ark?

16. In the Bible, Cain and Abel were brothers. Which one was the murderer?

17. Which rich queen made a famous visit to Solomon?

18. In the book of Genesis, a group of men built a tower. What was it called?

Quiz No. 27   **Sport**

1. In cricket, how many balls are there usually in an over?

2. For which sport is Sunningdale famous?

3. In rugby union, how many players from each team form the scrum?

4. Where were the 1980 Olympic Games held?

5. For which sport did Joe Louis become famous?

6. How many circles are there in the Olympic symbol?

7. For what sport is Gordon Pirie remembered?

8. In which sport was Randolph Turpin a champion?

9. From which country did the young gymnast Nadia Comeneci come?

10. In which sport was Sir Donald Bradman famous?

11. With which sport is Reg Harris associated?

12. In which sport might you be awarded a black belt?

13. How many players are there on a baseball team?

14. How many players are there on a British lacrosse team?

15. Who was the first athlete to run the mile in less than four minutes?

16. In which sport is the America's Cup competed for?

17. In which city is the Longchamps race course?

18. Which sport is traditionally known as 'The Sport of Kings'?

Quiz No. 28 General Knowledge 10

1. In which book do we meet the Mad Hatter and the March Hare?

2. Stalactites and stalagmites — which grow upwards?

3. How many is three score years and ten?

4. Of which country is Salisbury the capital?

5. What is backgammon?

6. What is a chandelier?

7. What is an 'Iron Horse'?

8. On what is a mural painted?

9. Whereabouts does a fish have its dorsal fin?

10. What is meant by 'doing a moonlight flit'?

11. In which country is Cook Mountain?

12. In which direction would a retrograde step take you?

Classical mythology
13. In mythology, who was Polyphemus?

14. Who killed Medusa?

15. What is the weapon called that King Neptune carries?

16. In Roman mythology, who was the god of war?

17. Of what sport was Diana the goddess?

18. Who flew too near the sun and melted his wings?

Quiz No. 29　The Calendar

1. On what date is St Valentine's Day each year?

2. On what date does Hallowe'en occur?

3. By what other name is St Stephen's Day generally known?

4. What is Hogmanay?

5. What date is St Patrick's Day?

6. When is St. George's Day?

7. October 21st commemorates a famous naval battle – which one?

8. In which month each year is 'The Glorious Twelfth'?

9. Which special day follows Shrove Tuesday?

10. We often hope it won't rain on July 15th. With which saint is that day associated?

11. What is a decade?

12. How long is a millennium?

13. When is United Nations Day?

14. On what date each year do the United States celebrate their independence?

15. By what name is Mardi Gras generally known in this country?

16. In Britain, which month contains the longest day?

17. After whom is the month of July named?

18. After whom is the month of August named?

Quiz No. 31   General Knowledge 11

1.   Who or what is a bachelor?

2.   What kind of languages are Cobol and Basic?

3.   What kind of dog is a Jack Russell?

4.   In education, what is meant by the initials PE?

5.   How many is a 'baker's dozen'?

6.   Which language did Julius Caesar speak?

7.   In art or painting, what is a primer?

8.   What colour do you get if you mix red and yellow paint?

9.   What colour do you get if you mix red and blue paint?

10. What colour do you get if you mix blue and yellow paint?

11. What colour is suggested by the word 'verdant'?

12. What colour is suggested by the name 'Rufus'?

13. According to the song, what was the colour of the boat in which the Owl and Pussy-Cat went to sea?

14. What is meant by the phrase 'Hobson's Choice'?

15. Who designed and engineered the Suez Canal?

16. Which town is generally said to be the centre of the American car industry?

17. Who claimed that 'History is bunk'?

18. The zloty is the unit of currency of which country?

Quiz No. 32 Capitals

1. What is the capital of West Germany?

2. What is the capital of Belgium?

3. What is the capital of Norway?

4. What is the capital of Poland?

5. Of which country is Lisbon the capital?

6. Of which country is Sofia the capital?

7. Which capital city stands on the River Tiber?

8. Which capital city stands on the River Liffey?

9. Of which island is Bridgetown the capital?

10. Of which island is Honolulu the capital?

11. What is the federal capital of Malaysia?

12. Within which other capital city is Vatican City?

13. What is the capital of Burma?

14. What is the capital of India?

15. Of which country is Port of Spain the capital?

16. Of which country is Lagos the capital?

17. Of which country is Caracas the capital?

18. Of which country is Buenos Aires the capital?

Quiz No. 33   Nursery Rhymes

1. How many bags of wool came from the Black Sheep?

2. Who was frightened by a spider when eating curds and whey?

3. Who sat on a wall and had a great fall?

4. Who stole a pig and then ran away?

5. How much did the Bells of St Martins say was owing?

6. What happened when Jack fell down the hill?

7. Who sang for his supper?

8. Who found a crooked sixpence?

9. Where was little Polly Flinders sitting?

10. Who killed Cock Robin?

11. Who laughed when the cow jumped over the moon?

12. What are little girls made of?

13. Who kissed the girls and made them cry?

14. Who runs through the town, upstairs and downstairs, in his nightgown?

15. How many men did the Grand Old Duke of York have?

16. How many men were on a dead man's chest?

17. How many blackbirds were baked in a pie?

18. Which amphibian went a-wooing?

Quiz No. 34 General Knowledge 12

1. Who live in wigwams?

2. Who or what is Shanks's pony?

3. What is, or was, the Luftwaffe?

4. How many Gospels are there in the Bible?

5. What are whitebait?

6. Which range of mountains is known as the Backbone of England?

7. Which is the longer: an ordinary mile or a nautical mile?

8. Who wrote *The Hobbit?*

9. For what drink is Vichy famous?

10. Who first said, 'We shall fight on the beaches, we shall fight on the landing grounds'?

11. What is a 'dramatis personae'?

12. What is 'foolscap'?

Drinks
13. What colour is a 'rosé' wine?

14. What is meant if a wine is labelled 'sec'?

15. What is the basic ingredient of the drink mead?

16. With which country is vodka particularly associated?

17. From which grain is whisky usually made?

18. What colour is a 'vin blanc'?

Quiz No. 35   **Science 1**

1. Where does solar energy come from?

2. In modern three-core electric cables, what colour is the 'earth'?

3. At home, where would you have a cathod ray tube?

4. For which gas is O the chemical symbol?

5. What colour light is made by all the colours of the spectrum together?

6. Which metal will flow without being heated?

7. In which branch of physics did Faraday become famous?

8. What is measured on the Richter scale?

9. In magnetism, do 'unlike' poles attract or repel?

10. What happens in a vortex?

11. For what is Na the chemical symbol?

12. Geology is the study of what?

13. What is measured in ergs?

14. For what precious metal are the letters Au the chemical symbol?

15. Where would you carry out investigations in a bathysphere?

16. What does an anemometer measure?

17. What do you study if you are a vulcanologist?

18. In what unit is electrical resistance measured?

Quiz No. 36   Sayings

1. What is 'crying wolf'?

2. What is 'money for jam'?

3. What is meant by 'a fly in the ointment'?

4. What do we do if we 'pull the wool over someone's eyes'?

5. What do we do if we say we hold out the olive branch to someone?

6. Which organization has 'Be Prepared' as its motto?

7. According to the saying, what animal might you buy in a poke?

8. According to the old saying, if the month of March comes in like a lion, how will it go out?

9. What is meant by 'minding your Ps and Qs'?

10. What do you do if you 'cross' someone's palm?

11. What is meant by the saying 'To shake the dust from your feet'?

12. In which story did a door open to the magic phrase 'Open Sesame'?

13. Who is supposed to have said 'Kiss Me, Hardy' just before dying?

14. Who said 'Elementary, my dear Watson'?

15. Who is reputed to have said 'Dr Livingstone I presume'?

16. Who wrote the words 'The workers have nothing to lose but their chains'?

17. Who first said 'Veni, vidi, vici' — 'I came, I saw, I conquered'?

18. Who said, 'Father, I cannot tell a lie'?

Quiz No. 37   General Knowledge 13

1. Which compass point is directly opposite East-South-East?

2. In which country are Maine and Alaska?

3. On which country's flag can you see the Star of David?

4. What is 'terra firma'?

5. Of what animal is a Dobermann Pinscher a breed?

6. What colour and value was the first postage stamp?

Flags
7. Which country's flag is red and white, with a red maple leaf?

8. Which country's flag is white, with a red disc on it?

9. What three colours are there in the Dutch flag?

10. What three colours are there in the French flag?

11. What three colours is the Belgian flag?

12. What three colours are there in the Italian flag?
———
13. What is the Turkey Trot?

14. From which country does goulash come?

15. In the world of antiques, for what has Dresden been famous since the eighteenth century?

16. Which historical leader was known as the 'little corporal'?

17. Which angel foretold Jesus's birth?

18. In which city is the Brandenburg Gate?

Quiz No. 38 Collective Nouns

1. What do we call a collection of people in a church?

2. What do we call a collection of people in a theatre?

3. What word do we use to mean a number of lions?

4. What do we call a number of wolves?

5. What do we call a number of oxen working together?

6. What do we call a large number of sheep?

7. What do we call a number of geese?

8. What do we call a number of new-born puppies?

9. What do we call a large group of locusts?

10. What do we call a large number of herrings?

11. What word do we use to mean a number of arrows?

12. What do we call a number of loaves of bread?

13. What do we call a herd of whales?

14. What do we call a group of partridges?

15. What do we call a group of magistrates?

16. What do we call a group of company directors?

17. What do we call a group of leopards?

18. What do we call a number of nightingales?

Quiz No. 39　Music

1. With which group of islands do we associate calypsos?

2. What sort of instrument is a Stradivarius?

3. What is the national anthem of France?

4. Of which country is 'The Maple Leaf Forever' a national song?

5. In a song, whose 'soul goes marching on' though his body is dead?

6. In which North American city is jazz supposed to have been born?

7. What musical instrument would a tympanist play?

8. What instrument is played by a flautist?

9. With which musical instrument is the name Bechstein usually associated?

10. Which musical instrument was invented by Adolphe Sax?

11. On which musical instrument would you be most likely to play a pibroch?

12. How many strings has a violin?

13. In music, what is meant by the term 'forte'?

14. In music, what is meant by 'pianissimo'?

15. What is meant by the musical term 'largo'?

16. What does the musical term 'crescendo' mean?

17. In music, what is meant by 'presto'?

18. What is meant by the musical term 'allegro'?

Quiz No. 40 General Knowledge 14

1. In which city is Lady Godiva supposed to have made her famous ride on horseback?

2. What couldn't you do if you were 'illiterate'?

3. In which continent is the Ivory Coast?

4. How many different signs are there in the Zodiac?

5. Which English king won the Battle of Agincourt?

6. Which animal is often called 'The King of Beasts'?

7. What is the capital of Switzerland?

8. What is the capital of Malta?

9. What does a zoologist study?

10. What was a Sopwith Camel?

11. Where does an arboreal animal live?

12. In 1844, W.C.T. Dobson is said to have sent the first what?

Poetry
13. Which poet wrote about a dirty British coaster?

14. Which animal did Blake describe as 'burning bright'?

15. Which bird brought ill-luck to the Ancient Mariner?

16. Which famous English poet is buried at Grasmere in the Lake District.

17. To which bird did the poet Keats write an ode?

18. Who wrote 'Paradise Lost'?

Quiz No. 41   Dates

1. In which year did the English defeat the Spanish Armada?

2. In which year did Julius Caesar first invade Britain?

3. What terrible disaster struck London in 1665?

4. In which year did the Battle of Trafalgar take place?

5. In which year did VE Day occur?

6. In which year was Queen Elizabeth II's Silver Jubilee?

7. In which year was the American declaration of independence?

8. In which year was Magna Carta signed?

9. In which year was the Battle of Waterloo?

10. What event took place in France, on July 14th, 1789?

11. Which year is the title of a famous novel by George Orwell?

12. Which year forms part of the title of a famous overture by Tchaikovsky?

13. On what date in 44 BC was Julius Caesar murdered?

14. In which year was the first manned space flight?

15. Which famous French statesman died in 1970?

16. In which year did men first climb Everest?

17. In which year did men first land on the moon?

18. Which revolution began in 1917?

Quiz No. 42   In Space

1. How long does it take the earth to travel round the sun?

2. Which is the oldest satellite orbiting the earth?

3. Is our sun a planet, star or comet?

4. We say the moon waxes and wanes, which of these means 'getting smaller'?

5. Which country launched the first successful manned space-flight?

6. Who was the first man to set foot on the moon?

7. Which planet is nearest to our sun?

8. Which known planet in our solar system is usually furthest from the sun?

9. What do you call a group of stars?

10. How many days does it take the moon to travel round the earth?

11. What causes a solar eclipse?

12. Back in 1961, who was the first man to travel in space?

13. Which planet is sometimes called the Red Planet?

14. Which planet is nearest the earth?

15. In which direction does the tail of a comet point?

16. Which scientist first said the earth moved round the sun?

17. Approximately how many million miles is the sun from the earth?

18. What did Major White and Alexei Leonov both do in 1965?

General Knowledge 15

Money matters

1. How many old pence were there in a pound?

2. In old money, how many farthings were there in a penny?

3. What is the unit of currency in West Germany?

4. What is the basic unit of money in France?

5. What is the unit of currency in Japan?

6. How many cents are there in an American dollar?

   ———

7. What ingredient has been added to some water supplies to improve dental health?

8. What is the science called that deals with stars and planets?

9. Tagliatelle, ravioli and lasagna are all kinds of what?

10. What was invented by K.C. Gillette in 1901?

11. What was the occupation of the legendary 'Casey' Jones?

12. If a Brecon Buff hisses, what does a Khaki Campbell do?

13. For what drink is chicory sometimes a substitute?

14. Which is the largest: cello, double bass, or viola?

15. Which is the largest ocean?

16. Who became king of the Huns in 434 AD?

17. For the Ancient Greeks, what were the four 'elements'?

18. When made as a European dish, what are two of the main ingredients of a kedgeree?

Quiz No. 44 Spelling

Spell

1. Aerodrome
2. Agreeable
3. Argument
4. Banana
5. Bicycle
6. February
7. Mischievous
8. Parallel
9. Parliament
10. Permanent
11. Recommend
12. Unnecessary
13. Apparent
14. Auxiliary
15. Committee
16. Definite
17. Desperate
18. Dictionary
19. Embarrassed
20. Exaggerate
21. Existence
22. Paraffin
23. Privilege
24. Pronunciation
25. Rhythm
26. Colander
27. Desiccated
28. Isosceles
29. Mediterranean
30. Mississippi
31. Phlegmatic
32. Psychology
33. Resistance
34. Reveille
35. Indispensable
36. Surreptitious

Quiz No. 45   Soccer

1. From which country does the club Benfica come?

2. From which country does the club Ajax come?

3. What colour card does a referee show to indicate a player is being sent off?

4. From which country does Bayern Munich come?

5. How often does the World Cup take place?

6. From which town does a football team called Real come?

7. A famous Swiss football club is named after an insect. What is it?

8. Which English team is known as The Gunners?

9. Who won the World Cup in 1966?

10. Who won the World Cup in 1974?

11. Of which country's team in the 1966 World Cup was Eusebio a star?

12. In which country did the finals of the 1970 World Cup take place?

13. For which country did Pelé play?

14. For what do the initials FIFA stand?

15. Kevin Keegan was signed by which European club in 1977?

16. In which year was the World Cup first held?

17. Osvaldo Ardiles of Argentina was signed by which English Club?

18. For what do the initials UEFA stand?

Quiz No. 46   General Knowledge 16

1. Where is the English Association Football
    Cup Final played?

2. What is meant by 'toeing the line'?

3. In which part of your body is your tibia?

4. Which story-book character swam in a pool of her
    own tears?

5. What was the blue dye with which Ancient Britons
    painted themselves?

6. Which country do the All Blacks rugby union
    team represent?

Insects

7. Queens, workers and drones are all kinds of which
    creature?

8. How many legs has a common house-fly?

9. Where do mosquitoes lay their eggs?

10. Why does a spider spin a web?

11. What is the common name for the Crane fly?

12. What is the common name for the larvae of the
    furniture beetle?

13. Which war began in 1950?

14. Whereabouts does a fish have its pelvic fin?

15. In London, what is the Old Vic?

16. What is meant by the Latin phrase 'in camera'?

17. Which of Shakespeare's plays involves a pound of
    flesh?

18. In which year did Britain have three kings?

Quiz No. 47   England

1. Which was the home town of William Shakespeare?

2. Which English port is famous for its White Cliffs?

3. What is Whipsnade famous for?

4. For what industry is Sheffield especially famous?

5. Which county used to be divided into Ridings?

6. Which English county is known as 'Glorious'?

7. In a song, with which fair in Devon is Tom Pearce associated?

8. Which is England's largest lake?

9. Which English county is chiefly associated with tin-mining?

10. In which English city are the High Level, Tyne and Swing bridges?

11. Which is the most westerly point on the English mainland?

12. Which is the most southerly point on the English mainland?

13. On Salisbury Plain there is a large and famous Bronze Age monument. What is it called?

14. In the West Country, what is a 'tor'?

15. What is the name of the island in the Thames where Magna Carta was signed by King John?

16. With which English city do you connect the name 'Sarum'?

17. Which Derbyshire town is famous for a crooked spire?

18. Name two of the English Metropolitan Counties.

Quiz No. 48   Hobbies

1. A Suffolk Punch, Arab and Percheron are all different breeds of which animal?

2. In which English town does the annual Veteran Car Run end each year?

3. About what would you be seeking information if you consulted Gibbons' Catalogue?

4. What is a tango?

5. How many dancers take part in a *pas de deux?*

6. What colour were all the early Model 'T' Fords?

7. Between which two towns was the railway line that carried Stephenson's first steam locomotive?

8. On board a sailing ship, what are the 'sheets'?

9. What do we call the skill of making patterns by inlaying different coloured pieces of wood?

10. What would you be arranging if you were doing 'ikebana'?

11. Plain, purl and moss are all kinds of what?

12. What is a campanologist?

13. What does a botanist study?

14. What does a philatelist collect?

15. What does a lepidopterist study?

16. What does an entomologist study?

17. What does a numismatist collect?

18. If you study calligraphy, in what are you interested?

Quiz No. 49   General Knowledge 17

1. What do Blackpool, Paris and Pisa have in common?

2. In which year did the First World War start?

3. Which animal is known as 'The Ship of the Desert?

4. In which book did William the First record a survey of England?

5. What was Istanbul formerly called?

6. If there is a curfew at night, what do you have to do?

7. Is talcum powder animal, vegetable or mineral?

8. In which country would you find the Pampas?

9. With which country is the famous soldier Robert Clive chiefly associated?

10. The Great Barrier Reef is off the coast of which country?

11. In which country would you expect to find people using a boomerang?

12. In mythology, who was known as 'the winged messenger'?

The human body
13. Where in your body is your retina?

14. How many bones can you move inside your head?

15. Whereabouts in your body is the bone known as the 'sternum'?

16. What happens if you inhale chloroform?

17. Whereabouts in your leg is your Achilles tendon?

18. In your body, what do arteries do?

Quiz No. 50 Explorers

1. Which famous explorer sailed on the 'Golden Hind'?

2. Which continent was explored by David Livingstone?

3. Which part of the world did Sir Ernest Shackleton explore?

4. Which explorer is said to have introduced tobacco into this country?

5. Name the ship in which Captain Scott made his first Antarctic expedition.

6. Whose ship was the first to sail right round the world?

7. Which explorer sailed to Australia in a ship called the 'Endeavour'?

8. In 1610, which explorer discovered Hudson Bay?

9. Which famous expedition in 1947 was led by Thor Heyerdahl?

10. Which famous scientist set sail in a ship called the 'Beagle'?

11. Who discovered the sea route to India via South Africa?

12. Who first reached the South Pole?

13. Which famous explorer sailed to the West Indies in the 'Santa Maria'?

14. What nationally was Christopher Columbus?

15. Who first sailed alone around the world?

16. Who first sailed non-stop round the world?

17. Who was the famous medieval traveller who left Venice in 1271 to explore Asia?

18. Which large island is said to have been discovered by Eric the Red?

Quiz No. 51   Scotland

1. On which river is Glasgow situated?

2. Which industry do you principally associate with the River Clyde?

3. Into which sea does the River Forth flow?

4. Off which coast of Scotland are the Hebrides?

5. By what name is King Robert I of Scotland often known?

6. Which city has or had the nickname of 'Auld Reekie'?

7. In which city are the administrative headquarters of the Lothian region of Scotland?

8. Of which Scottish region is Inverness the capital?

9. Which city is known as the Granite City?

10. In which city are the Gorbals?

11. Which city is overlooked by Arthur's Seat?

12. In which Scottish region is Ben Nevis?

13. On what date do Burns Night celebrations take place each year?

14. Which islands does the Pentland Firth separate from the mainland of Scotland.

15. On which river does Balmoral stand?

16. Which is Scotland's largest loch?

17. In which group of islands is Fair Isle?

18. With which craft do you associate Fair Isle?

Quiz No. 52   General Knowledge 18

Emblems

1. Which plant is the emblem of Ireland?

2. Which flower is the emblem of Scotland?

3. The white rose is the emblem of which English county?

4. Which country is represented by a hammer and sickle?

5. Which vegetable is the emblem of Wales?

6. In Christianity, which bird is sometimes used as a symbol of the Holy Ghost?

7. By what other name is a viper known?

8. Which mythological beast, half man half bull, was killed by Theseus?

9. What would you do with 'winkle-pickers'?

10. In which war did Florence Nightingale attend to the wounded?

11. In 1932, where was a famous Harbour Bridge opened?

12. Forties, Ninian, Frigg and Ekofisk are all what?

13. For what is Henry Moore famous?

14. How would you recognize an African rhino?

15. Which famous writers lived in Haworth Parsonage in Yorkshire?

16. Which important event happened in Dallas, in November 1963?

17. Into which sea does the River Danube flow?

18. Which day of the week is named after Saturn?

Quiz No. 53   Famous People

1. Who founded the Boy Scout movement?

2. For what was Houdini famous?

3. In what activity did Amy Johnson achieve fame?

4. For what was Isambard Kingdom Brunel famous?

5. For what was Sir Thomas Beecham famous?

6. With which art do you connect Marie Rambert?

7. For what discovery is Marie Curie famous?

8. In which art has Barbara Hepworth become famous?

9. With what in particular do you associate the engineer James Brindley?

10. In which industry has Richard Attenborough become famous?

11. Who succeeded Lenin as leader of Russia in 1924?

12. Was Pythagoras a famous sculptor, mathematician or playwright?

13. For which art was Caruso famous?

14. Which famous Russian revolutionary was assassinated in Mexico?

15. The ancient Greek Diogenes supposedly lived in what?

16. For what was Capability Brown famous?

17. Paderewski was once Prime Minister of Poland. He was also a famous what?

18. For what was Sir Henry Irving famous?

Quiz No. 54   Food 2

1. What colour does cochineal turn food?

2. In what are onions usually pickled?

3. With which meat is Yorkshire Pudding traditionally eaten?

4. What do we call the meat of a calf when served at table?

5. What kind of food is vichyssoise?

6. If you add chilli powder to a dish, would it make it hot or cold?

7. For what do we usually use a percolator?

8. From which animal do we get gammon?

9. For what kind of food is Roquefort famous?

10. Of what is a Pontefract cake made?

11. What colour is demerara sugar?

12. What is the proper fuel to use in a traditional barbecue?

13. In cookery, what is meant by 'coddling'?

14. What is meant by 'basting'?

15. What are 'escargots'?

16. Belle Hélène is a way of serving which fruit?

17. From which country does Canterbury lamb come?

18. What name is given to food prepared according to Jewish law?

Quiz No. 55   General Knowledge 19

1. How many days are there in the month of July?

2. Who is your closest maternal relative?

3. What kind of transport was a penny-farthing?

4. In the story, what was Cinderella's coach made of?

5. What is a 'jaywalker'?

6. What would you usually do with a Knickerbocker Glory?

7. What are Stedman triples, Plain Bob Caters and Grandsire triples?

8. In what are natural pearls found?

9. In history, who 'singed the King of Spains's beard'?

10. Does an earthworm have ears or eyes?

11. With what do we connect the terms AC and DC?

12. In which year did Queen Elizabeth II begin ruling?

The law
13. By what abbreviation is the International Criminal Police Commission usually known?

14. What crime is sometimes known as GBH?

15. What is the legal term for telling lies under oath?

16. What do you do if you commit blackmail?

17. What crime does an arsonist commit?

18. Where does the International Court of Justice normally meet?

Quiz No. 56   Fiction

1. In the novel by Henry Williamson what kind of animal was Tarka?

2. In a novel by Richard Adams, what sort of animal is Hazel?

3. In which book by Anna Sewell did a horse supposedly write about himself?

4. In which book do we meet Toad, Rat and Mole?

5. What was the first sign Robinson Crusoe had that there was another man on his island?

6. R.M. Ballantyne wrote a book about a desert island. What was it called?

7. In literature, who is partner to Dr Watson?

8. What are the two cities in Charles Dickens's *Tale of Two Cities*?

9. Complete the following title of the book by Jane Austen: *Pride and* ......

10. What kind of creature was Moby Dick?

11. In Stevenson's story of Jekyll and Hyde, which was the evil one?

12. According to the title of the famous novel, how many musketeers were there?

13. Whose mines were discovered by Allan Quartermain, Henry Curtis and John Good?

14. Name the old miser in Dickens's *A Christmas Carol*?

15. What monster was created by the novelist Mary Shelley?

16. In which novel is John Ridd the central male character?

17. In a novel, whose servant was Sancho Panza?

18. In the books by Leslie Charteris, by what nickname is Simon Templer known?

Quiz No. 57   Sport 2

1. In which sport do you use a puck?

2. What game would you play at the Royal and Ancient Club, St Andrew's, in Scotland?

3. For what sport is Henley famous?

4. In which sport is the Davis Cup played for?

5. In which sport do lions play wallabies?

6. In cricket, what do the initials MCC stand for?

What are the following associated with:
7. Straddle and Fosbury flop?

8. Little Mo and Maria Bueno?

9. Niki Lauda and Carlos Reutemann?

10. Butterfly and front crawl?

11. Jack Nicklaus and Tony Jacklin?

12. Goal defence and wing attack?

13. How many events make up the decathlon?

14. In athletics, which race commemorates a Greek soldier's run to Athens, when he brought news of victory in battle?

15. When were the first modern Olympic Games held?

16. How many events make up the Pentathlon?

17. With which famous steeplechase do you primarily associate the horse 'Red Rum'?

18. In which sport would you be taking part if you wore the 'yellow jersey' or 'le maillot jaune'?

Quiz No. 58   General Knowledge 20

1. What kind of food is scampi?

2. What do we call the chief member of the crew of a lifeboat?

3. What do we call a person who designs and plans buildings?

4. In the Bible, who was found in some bulrushes?

5. What is the highest mountain in Wales?

6. In sport, what do the initials LBW stand for?

Dancing

7. What kind of dance is the 'Blue Danube'?

8. Which dance is usually performed to Offenbach's *Orpheus in the Underworld?*

9. From which country does Flamenco dancing come?

10. Which dancing partner do you primarily associate with Fred Astaire?

11. Which city is said to be the birthplace of the waltz?

12. What kind of dance is a pavan?

13. On which river does Chester stand?

14. If a violinist was playing 'pizzicato' what would he be doing?

15. For what is Gerhard Mercater remembered?

16. What is the official national anthem of the United States of America?

17. According to legend, what are you meant to find at the end of a rainbow?

18. On their wedding day, besides something old, something new and something borrowed, what should brides wear?

Quiz No. 59   The New Testament

1. On which animal did Jesus ride into Jerusalem?

2. Which king tried to have the child Jesus put to death?

3. In which river was Jesus Christ baptized?

4. In the Bible, who are the four evangelists?

5. For how many days was Jesus tempted in the wilderness?

6. In which town did Jesus grow up?

7. Name the gifts brought by the Wise Men to the child Jesus.

8. Which disciple betrayed Jesus for 30 pieces of silver?

9. Which of the Apostles is sometimes nicknamed 'Doubting'?

10. In which town or village did Jesus turn water into wine?

11. When Jesus was crucified, who was the Roman Governor of Jerusalem?

12. What is the name of the hill where Jesus Christ was crucified?

13. Which of the disciples is described as one whom Jesus loved?

14. Who was the son of Elizabeth and Zacharias?

15. To which town was Paul travelling when he was converted?

16. Who first spoke the words known as 'The Magnificat'?

17. Which apostle was chosen to replace Judas Iscariot?

18. Who was the father of the disciples, James and John?

Quiz No. 60   Science 2

1. What happens at 0° Centigrade and 32° Fahrenheit?

2. What is measured in 'decibels'?

3. The letter H is the symbol of which chemical element?

4. What generates hydro-electricity?

5. Does a concave lens curve inwards or outwards towards its centre?

6. What is ecology?

7. What is measured with an altimeter?

8. What are recorded on seismographs?

9. What does a meteorologist study?

10. What is measured by a pedometer?

11. What happens when red litmus paper is put in an alkaline solution?

12. What can travel by conduction, convection and radiation?

13. After which famous scientist is a unit of electrical power named?

14. For what would you use a hygrometer?

15. With which scientist was the equation $E = mc^2$ first associated?

16. What is the common name for sodium chloride?

17. What travels at 186,282 miles per second?

18. What is measured on the Beaufort scale?

Quiz No. 61　General Knowledge 21

1. Which bear does Michael Bond write about?

2. Which country launches 'sputniks'?

3. In mathematics, what is meant by zero?

4. What is the capital of Japan?

5. According to the carol, on Christmas Day in the morning, how many ships came sailing by?

6. According to the song, on the fifth day of Christmas my true love sent me five what?

What is the modern equivalent for the old-fashioned word:

7. Yule?

8. Burgher?

9. Errant?

10. Benison?

11. Behest?

12. Betrothal?

13. A mule is a cross between which two animals?

14. What kind of animal is a pipistrelle?

15. In which continent is Israel?

16. In which city will you find the Trevi Fountain?

17. Who was the commander of the Allied Forces in Europe from 1943 to 1945?

18. What is unique about British postage stamps?

Quiz No. 62   Foreign Phrases

1. What is meant by vice versa?

2. What is meant by *post mortem*?

3. If you had *mal de mer* you would be suffering from what?

4. What is meant by the German word *kaput*?

5. What is meant by the phrase *coup de grace*?

6. What is meant by the French phrase *en avant*?

7. On which country's stamps would you find the word 'Helvetia'?

8. On which country's stamps would you find the words 'Magyar Posta'?

9. What is meant by the Latin phrase *vivat regina*?

10. What is meant by *sotto voce*?

11. What is *joie de vivre*?

12. What is meant by the phrase 'à votre santé'?

13. What is 'wanderlust'?

14. What is *savoir-faire*?

15. What is meant by the phrase *semper fidelis*?

16. What is the French phrase for *auf wiedersehen*?

17. What is the meaning of the word *eureka*?

18. What is meant by the Italian phrase *che sera sera*?

Quiz No. 63   **Botany**

1. What would you expect to find growing in a paddy field?

2. From which plant do we get molasses?

3. King Edward, Golden Wonder and Majestic are all types of what?

4. Do peanuts grow under the ground or above it?

5. Which plant do Colorado Beetles most often threaten?

6. Which of these are made from vegetable material: cotton, silk, linen, wool?

7. What is chlorophyll?

8. What kind of vegetables are 'shallots'?

9. Which plant is supposed to protect people from vampires?

10. In gardening, for what would you use a cloche?

11. From which plant is snuff made?

12. How many leaves are there on a shamrock?

13. What useful ingredient do broad bean plants put into their soil?

14. What kind of leaves do silkworms prefer?

15. What is special about a perennial plant?

16. What kind of plant is a biennial?

17. What is the common name for the plant from which we get belladonna?

18. What is Sweet Marjoram?

1. Which island is described as the 'Emerald Isle'?

2. For what do the initials UFO stand?

3. Which kind of spaniel is named after a king?

4. What is meant by the German word *Fúhrer*?

5. What is French for 'Christmas'?

6. In the Bible, what is an Epistle?

7. How many legs has a Bombay Duck?

8. According to the saying, what is there no need to carry to Newcastle?

9. Of what are 'quires' and 'reams' both measures?

10. How deep is a fathom?

11. In which book would you read about Long John Silver?

12. What is a *billet doux*?

Languages
13. Counting all its forms, which language is spoken by the most people?

14. Of which people is Romany the language?

15. What is the official language of the Argentine?

16. Which language is spoken in Austria?

17. Bengali, Urdu and Hindi are all native languages of which continent?

18. Swahili, Hausa and Bantu are all native languages of which continent?

Quiz No. 65   Geography

1. What are the distinctive features of a plateau?

2. Is the Tropic of Cancer north or south of the equator?

3. What name is given to the heavy summer rains in Asia?

4. What do we call a fertile place in the desert?

5. What is a typhoon?

6. What is an atoll?

7. In which country is the Camargue?

8. Which country forms the greater part of the Iberian Peninsula?

9. Of which country is Jutland a part?

10. Which are the three Benelux countries?

11. In which country are there 'polders'?

12. In which country is Waterloo, the battlefield where Napoleon was defeated?

13. In which continent is the Kalahari Desert?

14. In which continent is the Gobi Desert?

15. Name three of the countries that border the Baltic Sea.

16. Off the coast of which continent is the Spanish Main?

17. Of which country is the Peloponnese a part?

18. What is the name of the hot southerly wind that blows from the Sahara across southern Italy?

Quiz No. 66   Games 2

1. In which game do you pass 'Go' and collect £200?

2. What equipment would you need to play Cat's Cradle?

3. Normally, how many points do you have to score to win a game of table tennis?

4. What is a 'hat-trick'?

5. In which sport do both teams 'take the strain'?

6. With which children's game do you associate salt, vinegar, mustard, pepper?

7. In which game is the term 'stalemate' properly used?

8. What are mashies and niblicks?

9. What game was first played by Red Indians, then by Canadians, and came to England in 1865?

10. What number plays a vital part in the game of Pontoon?

11. Which colour ball in snooker counts the highest number of points?

12. If you consulted 'Wisden' about which sport would you be seeking information?

13. In which game do we use the terms 'pair', 'impair' and 'manque'?

14. For what are Tarot cards now used?

15. In which card game would you stick, twist or buy one?

16. With which game do you associate Spasky, Korchnoi and Karpov?

17. What sport would you practise if you were a toxophilite?

18. What do we call a period of play in polo?

Quiz No. 67   General Knowledge 23

1. In which continent is the Giant Panda found?

2. What is the capital of New Zealand?

3. Who invented a system of printed dots enabling the blind to read by touch?

4. What do we mean if we say a person is cantankerous?

5. What festival celebrates the coming of the Wise Men to the infant Jesus?

6. What was a Messerschmitt?

In the army:
7. What is a red-cap?

8. What is an RSM?

9. What does reveille indicate?

10. What is furlough?

11. What part of an army is the vanguard?

12. What do we call the tall fur hat worn by the Brigade of Guards?

13. What is a guru?

14. For which book was Samuel Pepys famous?

15. Of which country is Baghdad the capital?

16. In which war was the siege of Dien Bien Phu?

17. What is a 'farl'?

18. How many carats is pure gold?

Quiz No. 68   Geometry

1. How many sides has a rectangle?

2. How do you find the area of a rectangle?

3. What do we call a line which bisects a circle?

4. How many sides has a quadrilateral?

5. What word describes two straight lines that are always the same distance apart?

6. What is the radius of a circle?

7. What is the total number of degrees of the angles of a triangle?

8. What is an equilateral triangle?

9. How many sides has an octagon?

10. How many sides has a pentagon?

11. What do we call a triangle which has two sides (but only two) of equal length?

12. What will the formula πr^2 help you find?

13. How many sides has a rhombus?

14. How many degrees are contained in each angle of an equilateral triangle?

15. What do we call an angle of less than 90 degrees?

16. What do we call an angle of more than 90 and less than 180 degrees?

17. What do we call the side of a triangle that is opposite a right angle?

18. What is a tangent?

Quiz No. 69   Clothes 2

1. Whereabouts on your body would you wear spats?

2. Of what are clogs traditionally made?

3. Who were the first people to wear ten-gallon hats?

4. In which country would you expect to see women wearing a mantilla?

5. A fez is usually what colour?

6. Whereabouts would you wear a ruff?

7. Whereabouts on your body would you wear a stole?

8. What is a toupee?

9. Which women traditionally wear a sari?

10. Who has a trousseau?

11. With which city would you associate 'haute couture'?

12. What is a 'poncho'?

13. What are 'mules'?

14. Which item of clothing would you throw down as a challenge to a duel?

15. Nowadays, who might wear a wimple?

16. What are 'plus fours'?

17. What is a farthingale?

18. 'Unmentionables' was a nineteenth century nickname for what garment?

Quiz No. 70   General Knowledge 24

1. Which fruit is dried to produce raisins?

2. Which country is popularly known as the 'Land of the Rising Sun'?

3. In which sport might you have a caddie?

4. How many wives did Henry the Eighth have?

5. What is a dingo?

6. What word is used for the dormant condition of some animals in winter?

7. What do we call the narrow inlets of sea in Norway?

8. Which sea separates Sweden from Poland and Russia?

9. In which country is the Corinth Canal?

10. In which country is the Kiel Canal?

11. In which country is the Suez Canal?

12. Which famous international canal was opened to traffic in 1914?

13. What would normally come from the mouth of a gargoyle?

14. By what name is pickled sturgeon's roe better known?

15. In 753 BC, which city was supposedly founded by Romulus and Remus?

16. What would you normally do at an escritoire?

17. What is meant by the word 'diurnal'?

18. At which religious ceremony might a requiem be sung?

1. Which battle is recorded on the Bayeaux Tapestry?

2. Which peasant girl became leader of the French army and had the dauphin crowned at Rheims?

3. In history, which Indian city is famous for its 'Black Hole'?

4. In which famous battle did Henry the Fifth beat the French in 1415?

5. In which war did Cavaliers fight Roundheads?

6. What was abolished due to the efforts of William Wilberforce?

7. In what sort of shop is the Great Fire of London said to have started?

8. During which war was the Victoria Cross first awarded?

9. Which two countries were united by the Act of Union in 1707?

10. In 1812, which leader retreated from Moscow?

11. In which battle did Richard III lose his crown and the throne?

12. Which war was concluded with the Treaty of Versailles?

13. Which earl was known as the King Maker?

14. Which Prussian was known as the 'Iron Chancellor'?

15. What tax did William Pitt introduce in 1799?

16. Of which group of 'Martyrs' was George Loveless the leader?

17. Which English prince fought at the Battle of Crecy?

18. In 1819, in which English city did the 'Battle of Peterloo' take place?

Quiz No. 72   Animal Families

What do we call a young
  1. Frog?

  2. Elephant?

  3. Seal?

  4. Goose?

  5. Hare?

  6. Horse?

  7. What is the masculine equivalent of a heifer?

  8. What is a male sheep called?

  9. What is a male goose called?

10. What do we call a female rabbit?

11. What is the masculine equivalent of a mare?

12. What is a male duck called?

13. What is a female sheep called?

14. Hart and hind are the male and female of which animal?

15. What do we call a female fox?

16. What do we call a female swan?

17. What do we call young swans?

18. What is an elver?

Quiz No. 73   General Knowledge 25

1. In which sport is there a hooker, a stand-off and a scrum-half?

2. In what town was Drake playing bowls when the Armada was sighted?

3. In which continent is the Cape of Good Hope?

4. On which famous river does Cairo stand?

5. About which animal might someone shout, 'Thar she blows'?

6. Of what animal is a Pomeranian a breed?

7. What is a piazza?

8. Which straits separate Anglesey from Wales?

9. What event took place on 11th November 1918?

10. Who first transmitted transatlantic morse signals by radio telegraphy?

11. What have the kiwi, emu and penguin in common?

12. Which is the first book of the Bible?

Drinks from abroad
13. From which country does the wine Chianti come?

14. For what drink is Jerez famous?

15. From which country does the drink ouzo come?

16. From which country does the drink sake (*say* sah-ki) come?

17. With which country is sangria particularly associated?

18. From which town does the drink port take its name?

Quiz No. 74   Homes

1. Does the polar bear live in the Arctic or Antarctic?

2. Who or what live in a byre?

3. What do we call the 'home' of a fox?

4. What name is given to the 'home' of a badger?

5. What do we call the 'home' of a hare?

6. Who or what lives in a drey?

7. What do we call the 'home' of a beaver?

8. What creatures live in a formicary?

9. What do we call the home of an eagle?

10. Which country is the home of the yak?

11. Who or what live in a holt?

12. Who lives in a manse?

13. From where did the Incas come?

14. Where do troglodytes live?

15. Who lived in Valhalla?

16. Who lived on Mount Olympus?

17. Whose official residence is the Elysée Palace?

18. Whose official residence is Lambeth Palace?

Quiz No. 75   Slang and Dialect

1. What is a 'nark' or 'copper's nark'?

2. What is 'tommy-rot'?

3. What are 'digs'?

4. What is meant by 'mumbo-jumbo'?

5. What is meant by the slang word 'wonky'?

6. What do we mean if we say someone has 'kicked the bucket'?

7. What is meant by the expression 'to keep mum'?

8. If someone says they've been 'rooked', what do they mean?

9. Colloquially speaking, what are 'crocodile tears'?

10. What do you do if you put the 'kibosh' on something?

11. What happens if you 'get it in the neck'?

12. What is meant by 'sticking one's neck out'?

13. What does a journalist mean when he says he has got a 'scoop'?

14. A person who is said to be in 'Carey Street' is what?

15. If a man talks about his 'better half' to whom is he referring?

16. With which city do we associate 'Cockney' slang?

17. What is the Cockney rhyming slang for 'stairs'?

18. In Cockney rhyming slang, what is meant by 'plates of meat'?

Quiz No. 30   Pets

1. What is kept in an aquarium?

2. When referring to a horse or pony, what is meant by 'tack'?

3. Which mouse-like pet is noted for its cheek pouches?

4. What kind of pet is a chihuahua?

5. Angora, Chinchilla and Dutch are types of which pet animal?

6. Through what do fish breathe?

7. What kind of dogs are Airedales, Lakelands and Staffordshire Bulls?

8. How would you recognize a dalmation?

9. Traditionally, which kind of dog do Arctic explorers use?

10. Sussex, Cocker and Clumber are all types of which kind of dog?

11. What work is traditionally done by collies?

12. Which dog is traditionally a symbol of Britain?

13. What is a shubunkin?

14. On which animal would you normally use a curry-comb?

15. By what name are cavies often known?

16. Which animal is associated with the word 'canine'?

17. Which animal is often measured in 'hands'?

18. What is special about a rodent?

Quiz No. 76   General Knowledge 26

1. On the edge of which desert is the city of Timbuctoo?

2. In Paris, what is the Louvre?

3. What is the name of the great palace, south-west of Paris built by Louis XIV?

4. In which city would you find the Doge's Palace?

5. In which city is Topkapi?

6. In which Italian city would you find a leaning tower?

7. What is Reuters?

8. What is a gavotte?

9. What do Americans celebrate on the fourth Thursday in November?

10. Who was the famous architect who rebuilt much of London after the great fire in 1666?

11. What is the name of the capital of Tasmania?

12. What is the name of the capital of Jamaica?

13. Whom might you expect to see working in a 'dig'?

14. What is the Paris underground train system called?

15. The Authorized Version of which book was published in 1611?

16. Which writer created Sam Weller?

17. In the phrase, 'the quick and the dead', what is meant by 'the quick'?

18. By what popular name is Mendelssohn's 'Overture to the Hebrides' sometimes known?

Quiz No. 77   Inventions

1. In 1815, who invented the miner's safety lamp?

2. What means of communication did Alexander Graham Bell invent?

3. What was invented by Charles Macintosh in 1819?

4. What was invented by Robert Bunsen in 1852?

5. With which invention is Sir Frank Whittle chiefly associated?

6. Who is generally said to be the first man to have set up a printing press in England?

7. What was invented in 1851 by Isaac Singer?

8. With which industry is the inventor Henry Bessemer chiefly associated?

9. Who invented the petrol engine?

10. With what industry is the inventor Richard Arkwright associated?

11. What kind of road surface was invented by John Macadam?

12. Who invented the gramophone?

13. What form of transport was invented by C.S. Cockerell?

14. In 1926, which inventor gave the first public demonstration of television?

15. In 1884, what was invented by Lewis Waterman?

16. What was invented by E.G. Otis in 1852?

17. For what is James Watt famous?

18. What did the Montgolfier brothers invent in Paris in 1783?

Quiz No. 78   The World Wars

1. What is commemorated by VJ day?

2. What was the Gestapo?

3. By what popular name is 6th June, 1944 known?

4. In which year was the heroic evacuation of Dunkirk?

5. Which part of the British Isles was occupied by the Germans during World War II?

6. With which famous battle do we associate Biggin Hill?

7. Who invented the 'bouncing bomb' used by the Dambusters?

8. Which German battleship was involved in the Battle of the River Plate in 1939?

9. In World War II, who was the Italian Fascist leader?

10. What one event is generally said to have brought the United States into World War II?

11. In which war was the sea battle of Jutland?

12. In World War II for what was Baron von Richthofen famous?

13. On which two Japanese cities did the Allies drop atomic bombs in World War II?

14. In World War II, what were Gold, Juno and Sword?

15. In which town, in 1914, was an archduke assassinated?

16. Which cross was the symbol of the Free French during World War II?

17. Who was the Commander of the Free French forces during the last war?

18. In 1942, which island was awarded the George Cross?

Quiz No. 79   General Knowledge 27

1. What is a quadruped?

2. When a cow stands up, which legs does it get up on first?

3. Where is a person said to be sent when others ignore him?

4. What is bladder wrack?

5. Who is generally said to be the first Englishman to sail round the world?

6. What is your patella?

Hymns
7. With which festival do we primarily associate the hymn which begins 'We plough the fields and scatter'?

8. With which festival do we primarily associate the hymn which begins 'O come, all ye faithful'?

9. In the famous hymn, what line comes after 'Onward Christian soldiers'?

10. With which season do we primarily associate the hymn which begins 'Forty days and forty nights'?

11. The hymn beginning 'And did those feet ....' is known by the name of which city?

12. With which festival do we primarily associate the hymn which begins 'Christ the Lord is risen today'?

13. Which Civil War began in 1936?

14. In Scotland, what is a claymore?

15. In which Shakespeare play does Banquo's ghost appear?

16. Which king is said to have written the piece of music called 'Greensleeves'?

17. In ancient times what unit of measurement was the distance from elbow to fingertips?

18. What is meant by the phrase *tempus fugit*?

Quiz No. 80   Jobs

1. What does a drover do?

2. What is made or sold by a milliner?

3. What does a lumberjack do?

4. Where does a steeplejack work?

5. Where does a stevedore work?

6. What job is done by a concièrge?

7. Who uses a joy-stick?

8. What is a pedagogue?

9. In what trade would you find a compositor?

10. What does a farrier do?

11. What do we call a person who treats or cares for your feet?

12. What does a glazier do?

13. What is or was sold by an apothecary?

14. What job is done by a horologist?

15. What do we call a man who makes barrels?

16. What was an ostler?

17. If you are a cartographer, what do you make?

18. What does a brazier do?

Quiz No. 81   Rivers

1. On which river is Paris situated?

2. What is the longest river in Africa?

3. Which is the longest river in the British Isles?

4. Which is the longest river which flows entirely in England?

5. What do we call a small stream that flows into a larger river?

6. If a river is said to be meandering, what is it doing?

7. Through which capital city does the River Tiber flow?

8. Into which sea does the River Nile flow?

9. Into which ocean does the River Congo (or River Zaire) flow?

10. On which African river are the Victoria Falls?

11. In which country is the Yellow River?

12. On which one river stand the towns of Quebec and Montreal?

13. Which is the sacred river of the Hindus?

14. Of which country is the Murray the chief river?

15. Can you name the river on which both Belgrade and Budapest stand?

16. In which German river is the Lorelei Rock?

17. Which river flows through the Grand Canyon?

18. On which river is the Aswan Dam?

Quiz No. 82   General Knowledge 28

1. Which animal is known as Reynard?

2. To what would a manicurist attend?

3. What is unusual about a bonsai tree?

4. What would you buy at a 'box office'?

5. Which day of the week is named after the old Scandinavian god of thunder?

6. Of what is parquet flooring made?

7. What do whales eat?

8. What is the proboscis of an elephant?

9. What is a 'monologue'?

10. Which is the largest island in the Indian Ocean?

11. For what is Elizabeth Fry chiefly remembered?

12. What is the longitude of Greenwich?

The zodiac
13. What name is given to the sign of the zodiac which is usually shown as a ram?

14. The zodiac sign of Taurus is also known as the sign of the what?

15. How is the zodiac sign of Sagittarius usually shown?

16. What name is given to the sign of the zodiac that is usually shown as a scorpion?

17. The zodiac sign of Virgo is also known as the sign of the what?

18. How is the zodiac sign of Libra often shown?

Quiz No. 83   Legends

1. Which little girl was very nearly eaten by a wolf who was impersonating her grandmother?

2. How did Aladdin make a genie appear?

3. Who rid the town of Hamelin of rats?

4. Who shot an apple off his son's head?

5. Who was Robin Hood's chief enemy?

6. What is a vampire traditionally supposed to eat and drink?

7. In a fairy story, a queen had to guess the name of a little man or lose her baby. What was his name?

8. According to legend, whose drum sounds when England is threatened?

9. Who is said to have rid Ireland of snakes?

10. On which feast day did King Wenceslas look out?

11. Who is Beelzebub?

12. What is the name for the cup from which Jesus drank at the Last Supper?

13. Which legendary animal is like a white horse with a single horn?

14. Which legendary beast was half man, half horse?

15. What was Excalibur?

16. Who was the poet or magician at the court of King Arthur?

17. Who beheaded the Green Knight?

18. Above whose head was a sword suspended by a hair?

Quiz No. 84   Nautical

1. On which ship did Nelson die?

2. Which word describes the right-hand side of a ship, as you look ahead?

3. When is the Blue Peter hoisted?

4. On what kind of ship would a Jolly Roger have been flown?

5. Which famous liner struck an iceberg and sank on its maiden voyage in 1912?

6. If a sailor 'splices' two ropes, what is he doing?

7. Which was the first nuclear-powered submarine?

8. What is the name of the Royal Yacht?

9. If a ship is 'scuttled' what happens to her?

10. If a ship runs up a plain yellow flag, what does it mean?

11. What is the 'beam' of a ship?

12. On a ship, what is meant by 'abaft'?

13. In which city is the ship 'HMS Victory'?

14. Which famous modern sailor is associated with the yacht 'Gypsy Moth'?

15. Of which famous ship was William Bligh the captain?

16. What was the name of the ship in which Captain Cook sailed to Australia?

17. In which famous ship did the Pilgrim Fathers set sail for America?

18. What cargo did the 'Cutty Sark' carry?

Quiz No. 85   General Knowledge 29

Islands

1. In which group of islands is Tenerife?

2. Which island lies at the foot of Italy?

3. Off which coast of Africa is the island of Madagascar?

4. In which sea is the island of Cyprus?

5. In which ocean is Sri Lanka?

6. Name the island immediately south of Australia.

   _____

7. What kind of animal is a Persian Blue?

8. In London, what is the Tate Gallery?

9. What is 'café au lait'?

10. What is meant if you say you are 'at loggerheads' with someone?

11. Which religious faith observes 'Yom Kippur'?

12. What is Esperanto?

13. Which English city has given its name to a wheel chair and to a bun?

14. For what was Anna Pavlova famous?

15. In modern three-core electric cables, which wire is live?

16. Which people would fast during Ramadan?

17. Who wrote *Pygmalion*?

18. Which Russian author wrote a play called *The Cherry Orchard*?

Quiz No. 86   London

1. Where is the statue commonly known as Eros?

2. Which bridge in London opens upwards to allow tall ships to pass through?

3. Where are the Crown Jewels kept?

4. Where is Lord Nelson surrounded by four lions?

5. For what is Billingsgate famous?

6. Where is Speaker's Corner?

7. In which square are nightingales supposed to sing?

8. In which building is the Whispering Gallery?

9. In what general direction does the Thames flow through London?

10. What is the common name for the Central Criminal Court in London?

11. What is Lombard Street associated with?

12. In which street was Sherlock Holmes supposed to live?

13. What event is commemorated by the Monument?

14. What ceremony takes place on Horse Guards Parade on the Sovereign's Official Birthday?

15. Where is the Woolsack?

16. Who usually lives at No. 11 Downing Street?

17. In which building is Poet's Corner?

18. In 1829, what did George Shillibeer introduce in London?

Quiz No. 87   Proverbs

According to the proverb:

1. What should people who live in glass houses not do?

2. What is saved by a stitch in time?

3. At what do drowning men clutch?

4. One good turn ....

5. A bird in the hand ....

6. What kind of lane has no turning?

7. What can't you make out of a sow's ear?

8. Who may look at a king?

9. Who laughs loudest?

10. What makes Jack a dull boy?

11. What never boils?

12. Who blames his tools?

13. What will fine words not butter?

14. What is the mother of invention?

15. What is the road to hell paved with?

16. What kind of wind blows no good?

17. What was not built in a day?

18. What does familiarity breed?

General Knowledge 30

1. In a Punch and Judy show what is Punch's dog called?

2. On which date does Boxing Day fall?

3. What would you be if you used a lancet in your work?

4. How many arms has a starfish?

5. In which country would you be most likely to eat smorgasbord?

6. For what do the initials UHF stand?

7. Of which country was the fleur-de-lys once the emblem?

8. Which flower do you associate with Holland?

9. Which animal is the national emblem of South Africa?

10. Which bird was the emblem of the Roman Empire?

11. Of which country is the dragon a symbol?

12. What do we mean if we say we offer someone an olive branch?

13. Can you name two seas which are named after colours?

14. What nationality was the explorer Ferdinand Magellan?

15. In 1884, which famous statue was given to the United States by France?

16. With which Italian city was the artist Canaletto associated?

17. Who wrote the book *Peter Pan*?

18. Which has the largest ears, the Indian or the African elephant?

Quiz No. 89   Mathematics

1. How many metres are there in a kilometre?

2. How many centimetres are there in 3 metres?

3. What percentage is the fraction one-fifth?

4. How would three-quarters be expressed in decimal figures?

5. How many items make up a gross?

6. When you write down in figures the number 'one million', how many noughts are there?

7. What is the square of 20?

8. If you add together half a score and half a century, what do you get?

9. What do you call a frame of beads on wires used for counting?

10. What is the Roman numeral for the number 50?

11. What is ten per cent of a thousand?

12. What is the square root of 169?

13. Which is the larger — 5 dozen or 4 score?

14. If you add together half a dozen and half a gross, what do you get?

15. What do we call a number which cannot be divided by another number (except one) without leaving a remainder?

16. For which branch of mathematics was Euclid chiefly responsible?

17. In geometry what do the letters QED stand for?

18. What is the equivalent of a kilogram weight in pounds?

Quiz No. 90   Sport 3

1. How many players are there in a netball team?

2. In golf, what is a divot?

3. To which sport do the Queensbury Rules apply?

4. With what sport are Indianapolis and Le Mans both associated?

5. Which famous boxer was formerly known as Cassius Clay?

6. With which country is the Springboks rugby union team associated?

7. How many men are there in a rugby union team?

8. If you were using a spinnaker, what would you be doing?

9. For what sport is Bisley famous?

10. Which sport can take place on ice, sand or water?

11. In which sport would you win the Calcutta Cup?

12. How long is a cricket pitch?

With which sport are the following associated:
13. Greg Chappell?

14. Arthur Ashe and Rod Laver?

15. Joe Louis and Jack Dempsey?

16. Olga Korbut?

17. Bob Beaman?

18. Bernard Hinault?

1. How many days are there in the month of April?

2. Who is your closest paternal relative?

3. What is referred to as a four-poster?

4. By what name is Bruce Wayne of Gotham City better known?

5. Which city has canals instead of streets?

6. What is Kangchenjunga?

7. In which ocean is Madagascar?

8. What is the name of the ancient wall which crosses England from the Solway to Wallsend?

9. In what is a sword sheathed?

10. Greater horse-shoe, Whiskered and Long-eared are all types of which animal?

11. For what sort of book is Mrs Beaton famous?

12. Who was king of England from 1901 to 1910?

Foreign cities
13. Which city is known as the 'Big Apple'?

14. By what name is the city of St Petersburg now known?

15. In which city are the administrative headquarters of the Common Market?

16. What was the city of Volgograd once called?

17. What do we call the Italian city of Firenze?

18. Which city was built on seven hills?

Quiz No. 92 Mountains

1. Which is the highest British mountain?

2. In which range of mountains is Everest?

3. In which country is Mont Blanc?

4. In which continent are the Andes mountains?

5. Which is the highest of these: Mont McKinley, K2, Mont Blanc?

6. What is the name of the famous active volcano on the island of Sicily?

7. In which country is Vesuvius?

8. In which country are the Southern Alps?

9. In which country are the Snowy Mountains?

10. In which continent are the Atlas Mountains?

11. Which mountain range separates Spain from France?

12. Which famous mountain overlooks Cape Town in South Africa?

13. Which is the highest mountain in Africa?

14. In which sea is the volcano Stromboli?

15. In which country is the volcano Popocatepetl?

16. In which country is the Hill of Tara?

17. Which is the longest mountain range in the world?

18. In which country is Mount Ararat?

Quiz No. 93 Religion

1. At which religious service is a font used?

2. Which prayer is sometimes known as the 'Pater Noster'?

3. On which day does the Church celebrate the entry of Jesus into Jerusalem?

4. What do we call the forty days leading up to Easter?

5. What do Roman Catholics call the string of beads they use when praying?

6. For what is Oberammergau famous?

7. In what building do Jews meet for worship?

8. Of which religion is the Qu'ran the sacred book?

9. Of which religion is 'Zen' a form or sect?

10. Which Eastern religion includes the 'caste' system?

11. In which religion is Bar Mitzvah a ceremony?

12. What is the name of the holy city which was the birthplace of Muhammad?

13. By what name are members of the 'Society of Friends' often known?

14. Who was the founder of Methodism?

15. Which religious movement was founded a hundred years ago by General William Booth?

16. Which religious organization leaves Bibles in hotel rooms?

17. By what name are the 'Latter Day Saints' often known?

18. What were the priests of the old Celtic peoples called?

Quiz No. 94 General Knowledge 32

Colours

1. Name the seven colours of the rainbow.

2. Of what colour is kingfisher a shade?

3. Sepia is a shade of what colour?

4. Of what colour is saffron a shade?

5. Carmine is a shade of what colour?

6. Cobalt is a shade of what colour?
   ———

7. In what vessel would you pound ingredients with a pestle?

8. What would you most likely be buying, if you were 'gazumped'?

9. How many legs does a mongoose have?

10. Which is the largest planet in our solar system?

11. Who discovered penicillin in 1928?

12. In which ocean is the International Date Line?

13. Don Juan was a famous what?

14. In which of Dickens's novels do we meet Mr Micawber?

15. In Shakespeare, of which country was Hamlet supposedly a prince?

16. Which English king had the nickname 'The Hammer of the Scots'?

17. In which year did Britain join the Common Market?

18. Which of the five senses would be affected by something that was 'noisome'?

Quiz No. 95   Paraphernalia

1. What is a monocle?

2. For what would you use a parasol?

3. For what would you use a megaphone?

4. What do we call the oven in which a potter fires his pots?

5. What is the name of the stick used to conduct an orchestra?

6. What would you do on a pogo stick?

7. What would you be most likely to do with a hassock?

8. Where would you find a watermark?

9. Traditionally, what would you expect to find in a brazier?

10. For what would you use a brace and bit?

11. What is a rostrum?

12. How would you be most likely to carry a yoke?

13. What is 'pot-pourri'?

14. Where would you place an antimacassar?

15. What would you do with a besom?

16. What is a firkin?

17. What would you place in a bassinet?

18. What is a porringer?

Quiz No. 96   British Royalty

1. Which English king supposedly lost his jewels in the Wash?

2. Which British Queen fought against the Romans in AD 61?

3. Which king was inspired by a spider?

4. Which English king was known as the 'Confessor'?

5. Which English king supposedly ordered the sea to retreat?

6. Which English king supposedly burnt some cakes?

7. Who was King of England when Guy Fawkes tried to blow up Parliament?

8. Which King of England was known as Coeur de Lion?

9. How many of Henry VIII's wives were executed?

10. During whose reign was Magna Carta signed?

11. Which English queen never married?

12. Who was King of England from 1936 to 1952?

13. Which king reigned in Britain at the start of World War I?

14. Can you name a battle in which an English king was killed?

15. Which British king or queen ruled the longest?

16. Who was the husband of Queen Victoria?

17. Which king ruled in England from 1509 to 1547?

18. Who was King of England from 1660 to 1685?

Quiz No. 97   General Knowledge 33

1. What has a fuselage?

2. What do you do if you take a siesta?

3. Who might boast about doing 'a hole in one'?

4. Traditionally, which kind of dog is used for finding lost travellers in the Alps?

5. In the Bible, who was the Virgin Mary's husband?

6. On what does mistletoe grow?

Seas and Oceans
7. Which two oceans does the Panama Canal join?

8. What two seas are connected by the Straits of Gibraltar?

9. What two seas are connected by the Suez Canal?

10. What two seas are connected by the Straits of Dover?

11. Which strait links the Black Sea and the Sea of Marmara?

12. Which sea lies between Italy and Yugoslavia?

13. Name the capital of Iceland.

14. Who is usually credited with being the first man to reach the North Pole, in 1909?

15. What is meant by the word 'prodigal'?

16. What kind of precious stone is the Koh-i-noor?

17. Boswell wrote the biography of another famous writer. Who?

18. In a Roman 'triumph', what kind of crown did the Roman general wear?

Quiz No. 98   People

1. From where does a yokel come?

2. What do we call people born within the sound of Bow Bells?

3. Who would read Braille?

4. In which country would you be most likely to meet a 'colleen'?

5. Traditionally, how do Eskimos greet each other?

6. Who are the Mounties?

7. Who would meet in a coven?

8. Who might have a tonsure?

9. What did the 'forty-niners' go seeking in California?

10. In which country do the Basques live?

11. Of which country are Maoris the natives?

12. In which country were the Aztecs first found?

13. What is a quisling?

14. If we say someone is a Jeremiah, what kind of news does he always bring?

15. A kleptomaniac is a compulsive what?

16. What do pyromaniacs do?

17. What is a gentile?

18. In which continent did or do Hottentots live?

Quiz No. 99　Popular Music

1. Starr, Harrison, Lennon and McCartney were all members of which pop group?

2. Which group sang 'Save all your kisses for me'?

3. During which war did the song 'Tipperary' beome popular?

4. Which pop star was famous for his blue suede shoes?

5. Back in 1955, who rocked around the clock?

6. How many times does a normal long-playing record revolve in one minute?

7. With which group is Paul McCartney now associated?

8. Which singer had hits with 'Summer Holiday' and 'Congratulations'?

9. Which pop group first sang about living in a yellow submarine?

10. Mick Jagger is the lead singer of which group?

11. A well-known Swedish pop group has a name which reads the same backwards and forwards. What is it?

12. What would a musician use a 'plectrum' for?

13. Who is the most successful solo recording artist?

14. Which is the greatest selling gramophone record of all time?

15. Which musician was known as 'Satchmo'?

16. With which instrument do we associate Louis Armstrong?

17. Who wrote the music and words for *My Fair Lady*?

18. Who made famous 'Bridge over Troubled Waters'?

1. For what are P. T. Barnum and Bertram Mills famous?

2. With which country are the bagpipes associated?

3. In which continent do giant redwood trees grow?

4. What is a 'cock and bull' story?

5. What is a 'cloak and dagger' story?

6. In which country is the formation of rocks called the Giant's Causeway?

7. What fraction is a tithe?

8. Snap-dragon is a popular name for which flower?

9. What is made in a samovar?

10. What is a prima donna?

11. In Roman mythology what was the name of the god of the underworld?

12. In the Bible, who said, 'I find no fault in this man'?

The zodiac
Each sign of the zodiac is associated with one of the four elements of Earth, Air, Fire and Water.

13. Name two water signs.

14. Name two fire signs.

15. Name two earth signs.

16. What name is given to the sign of the zodiac that is usually pictured as two fishes?

17. The zodiac sign of Cancer is also known as the sign of the what?

18. The zodiac sign of Capricorn is also known as the sign of the what?

Answers

Quiz No. 1   General Knowledge 1
1. It is going out; receding   2. A lucky day, an important day
3. A dog (a Russian wolfhound)   4. King Arthur   5. Dollars
6. Waltzing Matilda   7. Greenland   8. Canada   9. The Atlantic
10. Greece   11. Corsica   12. St Helena   13. On a staircase (treads
— the flat parts, risers — the vertical parts)   14. British Broadcasting
Corporation   15. China   16. Rye bread (German)
17. The Aztecs   18. The earth

Quiz No. 2   Abbreviations
1. The United Nations Organization   2. Very important person
3. Répondez s'il vous plait; please reply   4. The Victoria Cross
5. SOS   6. On Her Majesty's Service   7. Anonymous, without a
name   8. Perambulator   9. Union of Soviet Socialist Republics
10. Please turn over   11. Cash on delivery   12. Central Intelligence
Agency   13. Heavy goods vehicle   14. South East Asia Treaty
Organization   15. European Economic Community   16. North
Atlantic Treaty Organization   17. Estimated Time of Arrival
18. The Roman army (Senatus Populusque Romanus)

Quiz No. 3   Aviation
1. Ireland (Eire)   2. West Germany   3. Belgium   4. Australia
5. Holland   6. Jumbo Jet, Jumbo   7. The height at which the plane is
flying   8. Paris   9. Rome   10. London   11. New York
12. Britain and France   13. Amy Johnson   14. Alcock and Brown
(in 1919)   15. Charles Lindbergh   16. (Louis) Bleriot (in 1909)
17. (Graf) Zeppelin   18. R101

Quiz No. 4   General Knowledge 2
1. Animal   2. You keep watch, keep awake   3. A small mountain
lake   4. Switzerland   5. The film industry   6. Harold   7. Rome
8. Paris   9. East   10. Welcome, hail, greetings   11. General
Gordon   12. Gold or silver (before it is made into coins. Bullion is also
gold or silver thread.)   13. Persia   14. Siam   15. Britain
16. Ceylon   17. Ireland   18. China (Northern China)

Quiz No. 5   Family Matters
1. 25 years   2. 50 years   3. Your mother's mother   4. Your
father's father   5. 100   6. A married woman whose husband died
7. Brother   8. Uncle   9. 8   10. Son of   11. Agnes or Vanessa
12. Sarah (Sally)   13. Frances   14. Gemini   15. A ruby
16. Diamond   17. 90 (or in the nineties)   18. Oedipus

Quiz No. 6   Birds
1. The Antarctic   2. The ostrich   3. The cuckoo   4. The owl
5. V formation   6. An aviary   7. Ornithology   8. The puffin
9. New Zealand   10. Geese   11. Swan   12. A canary
13. A parrot   14. The dove   15. The yellowhammer   16. The
albatross   17. The ostrich   18. The eagle (white-headed eagle, bald
eagle)

Quiz No. 7   General Knowledge 3
1. The hare   2. Usually, someone who is always reading (there is an

actual grub that eats books)   3. Vitamin C (there is also a small quantity of Vitamin B)   4. A helicopter   5. Russia   6. Brasilia
7. Apples   8. An apple   9. Orange, lemon, grapefruit, lime, citron
10. Sea food   11. A loganberry   12. A pomegranate   13. The kayak   14. Blue   15. Nero   16. A musical instrument (like a trombone)   17. Veal   18. George Gershwin

Quiz No. 8   Buildings
1. A mill   2. A brewery   3. A refinery   4. A moat
5. A window in the roof of a building   6. The front   7. Hops
8. The top   9. Above a door or window   10. In the basement
11. A castle (tower, fortress, walls)   12. To provide tombs for their rulers (also to house their belongings after death)   13. A tannery   14. An underground burial place, especially in Rome (underground gallery)
15. A window (an upright divider)   16. In a church-yard (at the entrance)   17. A castle (keep)   18. A distillery

Quiz No. 9   Films
1. Jerry   2. Spinach   3. Robin   4. A giant ape   5. Stan Laurel
6. Walt Disney   7. 101   8. *Star Wars*   9. 007   10. Tarzan
11. Sylvester   12. Bashful, Grumpy, Doc, Happy, Sleepy, Sneezy, Dopey   13. Pearl Harbour   14. Paul Newman and Robert Redford
15. The Keystone Cops   16. Al Jolson   17. Julie Andrews
18. Peter Sellers

Quiz No. 10   General Knowledge 4
1. 7 pm   2. 10 pm   3. 9.15 pm; quarter past nine   4. 8 pm
5. Quarter to midnight; 11.45 pm   6. 5.30 pm; half past five
7. Walking in single file (in the footprints of the man in front)   8. March
9. Swim the English Channel   10. He had a puncture   11. Your relations (members of your family)   12. Cana (in Galilee)   13. Japan
14. 10   15. Air travel (International Air Transport Association)
16. James I of England, VI of Scotland   17. *The Tempest*   18. A small pocket, watch pocket (watch)

Quiz No. 11   America
1. Sharp shooting, marksmanship   2. Davy Crockett   3. Texas
4. Tennessee   5. Petrol   6. Autumn   7. The Democrats and The Republicans   8. The Statue of Liberty   9. Abraham Lincoln
10. The American Civil War   11. California   12. New York
13. Nixon   14. Pennsylvania   15. Delano   16. David
17. Alaska   18. Texas

Quiz No. 12   Food 1
1. Cheese   2. Turkey   3. Sausages   4. An aubergine
5. Haggis   6. Vegetable (made from the roots of cassava)   7. To make it rise when it is baked   8. The white   9. A pepper (or spice)
10. Cabbage   11. Cream   12. Good Friday   13. Peas
14. Chips   15. A sausage (dry, cooked)   16. The stomach
17. Spain   18. Greece (Turkey, Middle East)

Quiz No. 13   General Knowledge 5
1. 26   2. P   3. Dick Whittington   4. 29   5. Asia   6. 50

7. A joey   8. A sow   9. Clergyman   10. Scots (especially Highlanders) (Irish)   11. Moscow   12. Pisa (Bologna)   13. They are all volcanoes   14. They are all types of knots   15. Cider   16. Tea   17. The Great Plague   18. 1588

Quiz No. 14   Animals
1. In its pouch   2. Its stripes   3. It has no tail   4. Fox
5. Upside down   6. It sheds some of its fur or feathers   7. The front legs   8. Bucephalus   9. The giraffe   10. The cheetah
11. Australia   12. One that is active at night   13. Pig   14. Cat
15. Whale   16. Cat   17. The elephant   18. Animals that can live on land and in water

Quiz No. 15   Games 1
1. Ludo and snakes and ladders   2. Table tennis   3. On a chess board
4. Nine   5. Ireland   6. Badminton ('Battledore and shuttlecock')
7. 16   8. Billiards (Russian pool)   9. Draughts   10. A hole done in one stoke under 'par' or 'bogey'   11. A castle   12. 52
13. Baseball   14. 50   15. 28   16. Poker   17. 15   18. Playing cards (matchsticks are often used for scoring, but not actually for playing the game)

Quiz No. 16   General Knowledge 6
1. Sweets   2. Wales   3. Animals   4. It has two humps   5. Sir Walter Raleigh   6. Ignore it, reject it, refuse to have dealings with it
7. 8   8. H   9. H   10. B   11. Alpha   12. Omega
13. The Boer War   14. George Orwell   15. Leonardo da Vinci
16. A semi-precious stone (a silicate, blue in colour)   17. Newfoundland, Labrador (Canada)   18. 7

Quiz No. 17   Art
1. Vincent van Gogh   2. Picasso   3. Paperfolding (modelling with paper)   4. van Gogh   5. Laughing   6. Whistler (James McNeill)
7. The Mona Lisa (La Giaconda)   8. Henri Toulouse-Lautrec
9. Thomas Gainsborough   10. William Turner   11. John Constable
12. Michelangelo   13. Spanish   14. Edgar Dégas   15. On a wall *or* ceiling (it is painted before the plaster is dry)   16. Leonardo da Vinci
17. Red, blue and yellow   18. The horse

Quiz No. 18   Composers
1. Beethoven   2. Johann Strauss   3. Tchaikovsky   4. Handel
5. Mozart   6. Bach   7. Beethoven   8. Schubert   9. Handel
10. Tchaikovsky   11. British   12. Poland   13. Mozart
14. Rimsky-Korsakov   15. Sibelius   16. Franz Joseph Haydn's
17. Beethoven   18. J. S. Bach

Quiz No. 19   General Knowledge 7
1. Fox hunting   2. Sailors   3. A builder, bricklayer   4. Christian
5. It sheds its leaves each year   6. Green, white and orange
7. Monkey   8. Fanatic   9. Venus   10. Aphrodite   11. Oriental
12. An autobiography is written by the person it is about and a biography is written by another person   13. Flesh, meat   14. Treason
15. Bigamy   16. A will   17. You have killed your father   18. You

have killed a king

Quiz No. 20   Associations
1. Newspapers   2. Theatres   3. The film industry   4. The diamond   5. Weddings   6. Christmas   7. Ballet dancing   8. Running or athletics   9. Painting   10. Opera singing   11. Classical music or violin playing   12. Writing books   13. Mortar   14. Jetsam   15. Fred Astaire   16. Mr Hyde   17. Peace   18. Lovers

Quiz No. 21   Clothes 1
1. American Indians (Red Indians)   2. A highlander (A Scotsman)   3. A man's hat   4. A full-length plain coat, worn usually by a priest   5. A wide-brimmed hat   6. On the head   7. The shoulder   8. Round the waist   9. A kimono   10. A veil or face covering (worn by Muslim women)   11. A mitre   12. An anorak (short weatherproof coat)   13. (Lord) Cardigan   14. Wellington   15. A (ballet) dancer   16. Mae West   17. A suit of armour   18. A man's close-fitting jacket, usually waisted

Quiz No. 22   General Knowledge 8
1. An acorn   2. XX   3. Grape (wine)   4. Oranges   5. Plums   6. An apple   7. The Danube   8. Models or projections of stars, planets, etc.   9. *The Sound of Music*   10. Liechtenstein   11. Originally a small musical instrument played by turning a wheel (barrel-organ) (street piano)   12. The leopard   13. A Scillonian   14. 6   15. The magpie   16. Carpets   17. Muslims, Moslems   18. Cat's eyes

Quiz No. 23   Authors
1. The (Just) William books   2. Enid Blyton   3. Beatrix Potter   4. Ian Fleming   5. Capt. W. E. Johns   6. Edgar Rice Burroughs   7. C.S. Forester   8. John Buchan   9. Jerome K. Jerome   10. Westerns (cowboy stories)   11. Agatha Christie   12. Raymond Chandler   13. Thackeray   14. Emily, Charlotte and Anne   15. Charles Dickens   16. Jane Austen   17. Karl Marx   18. John Bunyan

Quiz No. 24   On Holiday
1. A hotel for motorists (or road travellers)   2. Paris   3. Athens   4. Speak two languages (fluently)   5. Regents Park   6. France   7. Yugoslavia   8. Spain   9. Majorca   10. Morocco   11. Portugal   12. Italy   13. The Indian Ocean   14. Italy (it is in Milan)   15. Australia   16. Gare du Nord   17. The railway system (Société Nationale des Chemins de Fer)   18. Wine or vineyards

Quiz No. 25   General Knowledge 9
1. An unmarried woman   2. In a circus   3. The deer   4. On board ship   5. Cuba   6. Yes, every year   7. 2   8. The Union Jack   9. The death of a notable or respected person   10. New Zealand   11. The fifty states that now comprise the Union (The stripes represent the original thirteen states)   12. A harp   13. She was the first woman in space   14. Teeth   15. On its tail   16. At the South Pole   17. Groucho, Harpo, Chico, Zeppo and Gummo (these last two left early on)   18. Custer

Quiz No. 26   The Old Testament
1. Adam   2. Goliath   3. Noah   4. Daniel   5. The Garden of Eden   6. Joseph   7. Moses   8. The harp (or lyre)
9. Samson   10. Mount Sinai   11. Samson   12. A silver cup (a chalice or goblet)   13. A rainbow   14. A raven   15. 8 (Noah and his wife; his three sons and their wives)   16. Cain   17. The Queen of Sheba
18. The Tower of Babel (The Tower of Babylon)

Quiz No. 27   Sport 1
1. 6   2. Golf   3. 8   4. Moscow   5. Boxing   6. 5
7. Long-distance running   8. Boxing (light heavyweight)
9. Rumania   10. Cricket   11. Cycling   12. Judo or karate
13. 9   14. 12   15. Roger Bannister   16. Yachting   17. Paris
18. Racing

Quiz No. 28   General Knowledge 10
1. *Alice in Wonderland*   2. Stalagmites   3. 70   4. Zimbabwe
5. A game (using special board, draughts and dice)   6. A branched support for several lights or candles   7. A steam locomotive   8. A wall
9. On its back (or its top)   10. Removing furniture, or moving secretly, to avoid paying the rent   11. New Zealand   12. Backwards   13. A one-eyed giant (chief of the Cyclops in *The Odyssey*)   14. Perseus
15. A trident   16. Mars   17. Hunting   18. Icarus

Quiz No. 29   The Calendar
1. February 14th   2. October 31st   3. Boxing Day   4. New Year's Eve (December 31st)   5. March 17th   6. April 23rd   7. The Battle of Trafalgar   8. August (grouse shooting begins)   9. Ash Wednesday
10. St Swithin   11. 10 years   12. 1,000 years   13. October 24th
14. July 4th   15. Shrove Tuesday (Pancake Day)   16. June
17. *Julius* Caesar   18. *Augustus* Caesar (Caesar Augustus)

Quiz No. 30   Pets
1. Fish (or water plants, snails, etc.)   2. Its harness (saddle, girth, bridle, etc)   3. The hamster   4. A dog   5. Rabbit   6. Gills
7. Terriers (sporting dogs)   8. By its spotted coat   9. Huskies (Eskimo dogs)   10. Spaniel   11. Sheep-herding   12. A bulldog
13. A fish, goldfish   14. A horse   15. Guinea-pigs   16. Dog
17. The horse   18. It gnaws (like a rat)

Quiz No. 31   General Knowledge 11
1. An unmarried man   2. Computer languages   3. A terrier
4. Physical education   5. 13   6. Latin   7. A first coat of paint
8. Orange   9. Purple (or mauve or violet)   10. Green   11. Green
12. Red, reddish-brown   13. Green, pea-green   14. You have no choice at all   15. Ferdinand de Lesseps   16. Detroit   17. Henry Ford   18. Poland

Quiz No. 32   Capitals
1. Bonn   2. Brussels   3. Oslo   4. Warsaw   5. Portugal
6. Bulgaria   7. Rome   8. Dublin   9. Barbados   10. Hawaii
11. Kuala Lumpur   12. Rome   13. Rangoon   14. New Delhi

(Delhi)   15. Trinidad (and Tobago)   16. Nigeria   17. Venezuela
18. Argentina

Quiz No. 33   Nursery Rhymes
1. 3   2. Little Miss Muffet (Moffat)   3. Humpty Dumpty   4. Tom,
Tom the piper's son   5. Five farthings   6. He broke his crown
7. Little Tommy Tucker   8. The crooked man   9. Among the cinders
10. The sparrow (with his bow and arrow)   11. The little dog (laughed to
see such fun)   12. Sugar and spice and all things nice   13. Georgie
Porgie   14. Wee Willie Winkie   15. Ten thousand   16. 15
17. 24 (four and twenty)   18. A frog

Quiz No. 34   General Knowledge 12
1. North American Indians (Red Indians)   2. Walking; travelling on foot
3. The German airforce   4. 4   5. Fish (like small miniature herrings)
6. The Pennines   7. A nautical mile (approx. 800 feet longer)
8. J. R. R. Tolkien   9. (Mineral) water   10. Winston Churchill
11. The list of characters in a play   12. A size of paper (it originally had a
fool's cap as watermark)   13. Pink   14. It is a dry wine   15. Honey
16. Russia   17. Barley (rye or maize)   18. White

Quiz No. 35   Science 1
1. The sun   2. Green and yellow   3. In a television set   4. Oxygen
5. White   6. Mercury   7. Electricity (electro-magnetism)
8. Earthquakes (or the severity of earthquakes)   9. Attract
10. Everything swirls round, like a whirlpool (a vortex can be of any liquid or
gas or matter)   11. Sodium   12. The earth's crust or surface (rocks)
13. Energy (work)   14. Gold   15. Under water, in the sea
16. Wind speed   17. Volcanoes   18. Ohms

Quiz No. 36   Sayings
1. Raising a false alarm   2. Being successful without effort (or money
easily earned)   3. A detail, a trifle, that spoils everything   4. Deceive
or mislead them   5. Offer to make peace   6. The Boy Scouts
7. A pig   8. Like a lamb   9. Being careful to behave properly
10. Give them money (e.g. fortune tellers)   11. To show dislike of a place
(vow never to return to a place)   12. Ali Baba and the 40 Thieves
(Arabian Nights)   13. Nelson   14. Sherlock Holmes (Conan Doyle)
15. H.M. Stanley   16. Karl Marx   17. Julius Caesar   18. George
Washington

Quiz No. 37   General Knowledge 13
1. West-North-West   2. United States of America   3. Israel
4. Dry land   5. Dog   6. Penny black (twopenny blue)   7. Canada
8. Japan   9. Red, white and blue   10. Red, white and blue
11. Black, yellow and red   12. Green, white and red   13. A dance
14. Hungary   15. China, porcelain   16. Napoleon I (Bonaparte)
17. Gabriel   18. (East) Berlin (It is just inside East Berlin)

Quiz No. 38   Collective Nouns
1. A congregation   2. An audience   3. A pride   4. A pack
5. A team (or yoke)   6. A flock   7. A gaggle   8. A litter
9. A plague or swarm   10. A shoal   11. A flight (a quiver)

12. A batch   13. A school (a gam)   14. A covey   15. A bench
16. A board   17. A leap   18. A watch

Quiz No. 39   Music
1. The West Indies   2. A violin   3. 'La Marseillaise'   4. Canada
5. John Brown's   6. New Orleans   7. Drums (percussion instruments)
8. A flute   9. The piano   10. The saxophone   11. Bagpipes
12. 4 (G, D, A, E)   13. Strongly, loudly   14. Very softly
15. Slowly, dignified   16. The music should gradually become louder and
louder   17. Quickly   18. Fairly fast, lively, briskly

Quiz No. 40   General Knowledge 14
1. Coventry   2. Read or write   3. Africa   4. 12   5. Henry V
6. The lion   7. Berne   8. Valletta   9. Animals, animal life
10. An aeroplane (in the First World War)   11. In trees   12. Christmas
card   13. John Masefield   14. Tiger   15. The albatross
16. William Wordsworth   17. The nightingale   18. John Milton

Quiz No. 41   Dates
1. 1588   2. 55 BC   3. The Great Plague   4. 1805   5. 1945
6. 1977   7. 1776   8. 1215   9. 1815   10. The storming of the
Bastille   11. 1984   12. 1812   13. The Ides of March (15th March)
14. 1961 (Yuri Gagarin)   15. General de Gaulle   16. 1953
17. 1969   18. The Russian Revolution

Quiz No. 42   In Space
1. 365 1/4 days; 1 year   2. The moon   3. A star   4. Wanes
5. Russia   6. Neil Armstrong   7. Mercury   8. Pluto   9. A
constellation (galaxy)   10. 27 1/3 days (27 or 28)   11. The moon
passing between the earth and the sun   12. Yuri Gagarin   13. Mars
14. Venus   15. Away from the sun   16. Copernicus   17. 91-93
million (it varies – average distance: 92, 955, 829 miles)   18. Walk in
space

Quiz No. 43   General Knowledge 15
1. 240   2. 4   3. The mark (Deutschmark) (100 pfennigs = 1 mark)
4. The franc (100 centimes = 1 franc)   5. The yen (100 sen = 1 yen)
6. 100   7. Fluoride   8. Astronomy   9. Pasta   10. The safety
razor   11. Railroad engineer (engine driver)   12. It quacks. (It's a
duck; a Brecon Buff is a goose)   13. Coffee   14. Double bass
15. The Pacific, (165,240,000 square kilometres)   16. Attila
17. Earth, Air, Fire and Water   18. Fish, rice, eggs (as an Indian dish,
kedgeree also has onions, meat, lentils)

Quiz No. 45   Soccer
1. Portugal   2. The Netherlands   3. Red   4. West Germany
5. Every 4 years   6. Madrid   7. Grasshopper   8. Arsenal
9. England   10. West Germany   11. Portugal   12. Mexico
13. Brazil   14. Federation of International Football Associations
15. SV Hamburg   16. 1930   17. Tottenham Hotspurs (Spurs)
18. Union of European Football Associations

Quiz No. 46   General Knowledge 16
1. Wembley, London   2. Keeping the rules; submitting to discipline
3. Your leg (it is the shin bone)   4. Alice in Wonderland   5. Woad
6. New Zealand   7. Bees   8. 6   9. In water   10. To catch flies
11. Daddy-long-legs   12. Woodworm   13. The Korean War
14. Underneath it; on its belly   15. A theatre   16. Secretly, in private
17. *The Merchant of Venice* 18. 1936 (George V, Edward VIII, George VI)

Quiz No. 47   England
1. Stratford-on-Avon   2. Dover   3. Its zoo   4. Steel
5. Yorkshire   6. Devon   7. Widecombe   8. Windermere
9. Cornwall   10. Newcastle upon Tyne   11. Land's End   12. The
Lizard   13. Stonehenge   14. A hill, rocky peak   15. Runnymede
16. Salisbury   17. Chesterfield   18. Greater London, Tyne & Wear,
Greater Manchester, Merseyside, West Midlands, West Yorkshire, South
Yorkshire

Quiz No. 48   Hobbies
1. Horse   2. Brighton   3. Postage stamps   4. A dance   5. Two
6. Black   7. Stockton and Darlington   8. Ropes   9. Marquetry
10. Flowers, twigs, etc.   11. Knitting stitches   12. A bell ringer
13. Plant life   14. Postage stamps   15. Butterflies   16. Insects
17. Coins   18. Handwriting

Quiz No. 49   General Knowledge 17
1. They all have (famous) towers   2. 1914   3. The camel
4. The Domesday Book   5. Constantinople (Byzantium)
6. Stay at home or indoors   7. Mineral (magnesium silicate)
8. Argentina (they are vast grassy plains)   9. India   10. Australia
11. Australia   12. Mercury or Hermes   13. In the eye   14. One
(the lower jaw)   15. The centre of the chest   16. You become
insensitive (become unconscious)   17. At the back of the ankle (ankle)
18. Carry blood *from* the heart

Quiz No. 50   Explorers
1. Sir Francis Drake   2. Africa   3. Antarctica (South Pole region)
   4. Sir Walter Raleigh   5. 'The Discovery'   6. Ferdinand Magellan
7. Captain Cook   8. Henry Hudson   9. Kon Tiki   10. Charles
Darwin   11. Vasco da Gama   12. Roald Amundsen (Scott reached it a
month later)   13. Christopher Columbus   14. Italian   15. Joshua
Slocum (1895-8)   16. Robin Knox-Johnston   17. Marco Polo
18. Greenland

Quiz No. 51   Scotland
1. The Clyde   2. Shipbuilding   3. The North Sea   4. The west
coast   5. Bruce, Robert the Bruce   6. Edinburgh   7. Edinburgh
8. The Highland region   9. Aberdeen   10. Glasgow
11. Edinburgh   12. The Highland region   13. January 25th
14. The Orkneys   15. River Dee   16. Loch Lomond   17. The
Shetlands   18. Knitting

Quiz No. 52   General Knowledge 18
1. The shamrock   2. The thistle   3. Yorkshire   4. Russia (USSR)

5. The leek   6. The dove   7. Adder   8. The minotaur   9. Wear
them: they are shoes with pointed toes   10. The Crimean War
11. Sydney   12. North Sea oil fields   13. Sculpture or painting
14. It has two horns   15. The Brontë sisters   16. The assassination of
President Kennedy   17. The Black Sea   18. Saturday

Quiz No. 53   Famous People
1. Lord Baden-Powell   2. Escaping (from handcuffs, etc) (tight-rope
walking)   3. Flying aeroplanes (often solo)   4. Engineering (building
bridges, boats, railways, tunnels)   5. Conducting music   6. Ballet
7. Radium   8. Sculpture   9. Canal building, canals, aquaducts
10. The film industry   11. Stalin   12. Mathematician   13. (Italian)
Opera singing   14. Trotsky   15. A tub (barrel)   16. Landscape
gardening   17. Concert pianist   18. Acting

Quiz No. 54   Food 2
1. Red (pink)   2. Vinegar   3. Beef   4. Veal   5. Soup (often
eaten cold)   6. Hot   7. Making coffee   8. Pig   9. Cheese (goat
or ewe's)   10. Liquorice   11. Light brown   12. Charcoal
13. Simmering for a short while (e.g. eggs)   14. Pouring hot fat (or other
liquid) over meat while it is cooking   15. Snails   16. Pears (with butter
and chocolate)   17. New Zealand   18. Kosher

Quiz No. 55   General Knowledge 19
1. 31   2. Your mother   3. A bicycle   4. A pumpkin   5. A
pedestrian who ignores traffic regulations   6. Eat it (it is an ice-cream
sundae)   7. Ways of ringing church bells (or changes)   8. In oysters
(also in other molluscs)   9. Sir Francis Drake (by sailing into Cadiz
harbour)   10. No, neither   11. Electricity   12. 1952 (1953 was the
year of her coronation)   13. Interpol   14. Grievous Bodily Harm
(wounding, or intending to wound, a person)   15. Perjury
16. Demand with menaces (usually a demand for money)   17. He sets
fire to buildings   18. The Hague

Quiz No. 56   Fiction
1. An otter (*Tarka the Otter*)   2. A rabbit (*Watership Down*)
3. *Black Beauty*   4. *The Wind in the Willows*   5. He saw a footprint in
the sand   6. *Coral Island*   7. Sherlock Holmes   8. London and
Paris   9. *Prejudice*   10. A whale (white whale)   11. Hyde
12. 3   13. King Solomon's   14. (Ebeneezer) Scrooge
15. Frankenstein   16. *Lorna Doone* (by R. D. Blackmore)   17. Don
Quixote   18. The Saint

Quiz No. 57   Sport 2
1. Ice-hockey   2. Golf   3. Rowing   4. Lawn tennis   5. Rugby
(Union)   6. Marylebone Cricket Club   7. High jumping   8. Lawn
tennis   9. Motor Racing   10. Swimming   11. Golf   12. Netball
13. 10   14. The Marathon   15. 1896   16. 5   17. The Grand
National   18. Bicycle races (especially Tour de France or Milk Race)

Quiz No. 58   General Knowledge 20
1. Fish (large prawns)   2. The coxswain   3. An architect

4. Moses   5. Snowdon   6. Leg before wicket (in cricket)   7. A
waltz   8. The can-can   9. Spain   10. Ginger Rogers
11. Vienna   12. A slow and stately one, originally Italian or Spanish
13. Dee   14. Plucking the strings   15. Map-making (especially
projection of the world on maps) (mathematics or geography)   16. 'The
Star-spangled Banner'   17. A pot of gold   18. Something blue

Quiz No. 59   The New Testament
1. An ass or donkey   2. Herod   3. The Jordan   4. Matthew,
Mark, Luke and John   5. 40   6. Nazareth   7. Gold, frankincense
and myrrh   8. Judas (Iscariot)   9. Thomas   10. Cana (in Galilee)
11. Pontius Pilate   12. Calvary or Golgotha   13. John   14. John
(the Baptist)   15. Damascus   16. Mary (the mother of Jesus)
17. Matthias   18. Zebedee

Quiz No. 60   Science 2
1. Water freezes   2. Noise   3. Hydrogen   4. Water power (water)
5. Inwards   6. The study of the environment (the relationship of plants
and animals to their environment)   7. Height or altitude   8. Earth
tremors or earthquakes   9. The atmosphere (the weather)   10. How
far you walk   11. It turns blue   12. Heat   13. (James) Watt
14. To measure the humidity in the air   15. Einstein   16. Salt
17. Light   18. Wind force or speed

Quiz No. 61   General Knowledge 21
1. Paddington   2. Russia   3. Nought   4. Tokyo   5. 3
6. Gold rings   7. Christmas   8. Citizen (townsman)
9. Wandering   10. Blessing   11. Order   12. Engagement
13. Ass (or donkey) and horse   14. A bat   15. Asia   16. Rome
17. General Dwight Eisenhower   18. They do not show the name of the
country of origin (Britain is the only country in the world which does not put
its name on its stamps)

Quiz No. 62   Foreign Phrases
1. The other way round   2. After death   3. Sea sickness   4. Done
for, broken, finished   5. Finishing stoke; mercy blow   6. Forward!
7. Switzerland   8. Hungary   9. Long live the queen   10. In a low
voice, under your breath   11. Joy of living   12. To your health,
'cheers'   13. A longing to travel   14. 'Know-how', tact, skill in dealing
with people and situations   15. Always faithful, forever faithful
16. Au revoir   17. 'I have found it'   18. 'Whatever will be, will be'

Quiz No. 63   Botany
1. Rice   2. Sugar cane   3. Potato   4. Under the ground
5. Potato   6. Cotton and linen   7. The green colouring matter in
plants   8. A type of onion   9. Garlic   10. To protect plants,
especially from frost also to force plants   11. Tobacco   12. 3
13. Nitrogen   14. Mulberry   15. It lasts for several years   16. One
that lasts two years (it is planted one year and flowers and dies the next)
17. Deadly nightshade   18. A herb (used in cooking) (a plant)

Quiz No. 64   General Knowledge 22
1. Ireland   2. Unidentified flying object   3. A King Charles Spaniel
(King Charles II)   4. Leader (ruler)   5. Noël   6. A letter
7. None (it's a fish)   8. Coals   9. Paper   10. 6 feet (approx. 2
metres)   11. *Treasure Island* (by R. L. Stevenson)   12. A love letter
13. Chinese   14. Gypsies (travelling people, the Romanies)
15. Spanish   16. German   17. Asia (the Indian sub-continent)
18. Africa

Quiz No. 65   Geography
1. It is flat, high, land   2. North   3. The monsoons   4. An oasis
   5. A violent hurricane, especially in China seas (very strong wind)   6. A
ring-shaped coral reef (enclosing a lagoon)   7. France
8. Spain   9. Denmark   10. Belgium, the Netherlands, Luxembourg
11. Holland (land reclaimed from the sea)   12. Belgium   13. Africa
14. Asia   15. Denmark, Finland, Poland, Sweden, Russia, West
Germany, East Germany   16. (South) America (Central America)
17. Greece   18. The Sirocco (Khamsin)

Quiz No. 66   Games 2
1. Monopoly   2. A loop of string (or wool, cotton, etc)   3. 21
4. Three in a row (originally wickets in cricket, also goals, etc)
5. Tug-o-war   6. Skipping   7. Chess   8. Golf clubs
9. Lacrosse   10. 21   11. The black   12. Cricket   13. Roulette
14. Foretune telling   15. Pontoon   16. Chess   17. Archery
18. A chukka

Quiz No. 67   General Knowledge 23
1. Asia   2. Wellington   3. Louis Braille   4. He is quarrelsome or
bad-tempered   5. Epiphany (Twelfth Night)   6. A German fighter-
plane (bubble car)   7. A (military) policeman   8. A regimental
sergeant major   9. Time to get up   10. Leave of absence   11. The
foremost/front part   12. A bearskin (not busby)   13. A spiritual
teacher (usually Hindu)   14. His diary   15. Iraq   16. The Vietnam
War   17. A loaf (or oatcake; quadrant shaped)   18. 24

Quiz No. 68   Geometry
1. 4   2. You multiply its length by its breadth   3. The diameter
4. 4   5. Parallel   6. The distance from the centre to the
circumference   7. 180   8. One with all three sides of equal length
(with 3 equal sides)   9. 8   10. 5   11. Isosceles   12. The area of
a circle   13. 4   14. 60   15. Acute   16. Obtuse   17. The
hypotenuse   18. A straight line which *touches* a circle at one point, but
does not cross the circle

Quiz No. 69   Clothes 2
1. On your feet (ankles)   2. Wood   3. Cowboys   4. Spain
5. Red   6. Round your neck   7. Over the shoulders, round the neck
8. A (small)wig, hairpiece   9. Hindu (Indian)   10. A bride
11. Paris   12. A cape with a slit for the head; a blanket-like cloak
13. Slippers   14. A gauntlet   15. A nun   16. Knickerbockers
(trousers that tuck into socks, just below the knee)   17. A hooped under-
skirt   18. Men's trousers

Quiz No. 70 General Knowledge 24
1. Grapes   2. Japan   3. Golf   4. 6   5. A wild dog (Australian)
6. Hibernation/hibernates   7. Fjords   8. The Baltic Sea   9. Greece
10. Germany   11. Egypt   12. The Panama Canal   13. (Rain)
water   14. Caviare   15. Rome   16. Write   17. Daily   18. A
funeral

Quiz No. 71 History
1. The Battle of Hastings   2. Joan of Arc   3. Calcutta
4. Agincourt   5. The English Civil War   6. Slavery   7. A baker's
shop (in Pudding Lane)   8. The Crimean War   9. England and
Scotland   10. Napoleon   11. The Battle of Bosworth Field (1485)
12. World War I   13. Warwick (Richard Neville)   14. von Bismarck
(of Germany)   15. Income tax   16. The Tolpuddle Martyrs
17. Edward, the Black Prince (son of Edward II)   18. Manchester

Quiz No. 72 Animal Families
1. Tadpole   2. Calf   3. Pup   4. Gosling   5. Leveret
6. Foal (colt *or* filly)   7. A bullock (young bull)   8. A ram (wether)
9. A gander   10. A doe   11. A stallion (colt *or* gelding)
12. A drake   13. A ewe (tup)   14. Deer (especially Red deer)
15. A vixen   16. A pen   17. Cygnets   18. A young eel

Quiz No. 73 General Knowledge 25
1. Rugby (Union or League)   2. Plymouth   3. Africa   4. Nile
5. A whale   6. Dog   7. A square, an open space in a town or city
8. The Menai Straits   9. Armistice was declared (World War I)
10. Marconi   11. They are all birds that cannot fly   12. Genesis
13. Italy   14. Sherry   15. Greece   16. Japan   17. Spain
18. Oporto

Quiz No. 74 Homes
1. Arctic   2. Cattle   3. An earth (*or* lair)   4. A set (earth)
5. A form   6. A squirrel   7. A lodge   8. Ants   9. An eyrie
10. Tibet   11. Otters   12. A minister (Methodist or Free Church)
(clergyman)   13. Peru (South America)   14. In caves   15. The
Norse gods; plus Norse heroes   16. The Greek gods   17. The
President of France   18. The Archbishop of Canterbury

Quiz No. 75 Slang and Dialect
1. A spy, informer   2. Nonsense, rubbish   3. Lodgings, rooms
4. Meaningless jargon   5. Unsteady   6. He or she has died   7. To
keep a secret   8. They have been cheated   9. False tears or false
sorrow   10. 'Do for it', kill it off, end it   11. You get told off, you are
reprimanded   12. Asking for trouble; risking saying or doing something
13. He has an exclusive story   14. Bankrupt   15. His wife
16. London   17. Apples and pears   18. Feet

Quiz No. 76 General Knowledge 26
1. The Sahara   2. An art gallery   3. Versailles   4. Venice (there is
another in Genoa)   5. Istanbul   6. Pisa (there is another in Bologna)
7. A news agency   8. A stately minuet (a dance)   9. Thanksgiving
Day   10. Sir Christopher Wren   11. Hobart   12. Kingston

13. An archaeologist   14. The metro   15. Bible   16. Charles Dickens (in *Pickwick Papers*)   17. The living   18. Fingal's Cave

Quiz No. 77   Inventions
1. (Sir Humphrey) Davy   2. The telephone   3. Waterproof rubber/mackintoshes   4. The Bunsen burner   5. The jet engine
6. (William) Caxton   7. The sewing-machine   8. Steel
9. (Gottlieb) Daimler   10. Spinning (cotton) (He invented a spinning frame)   11. Tarmac   12. (Thomas) Edison   13. The hovercraft
14. (John Logie) Baird   15. The fountain pen   16. The lift (elevator)
17. The invention of the first (rotary) steam engine (1782)   18. The hot-air balloon

Quiz No. 78   The World Wars
1. The end of hostilities in the Far East (15th August 1945)   2. The Nazi secret police   3. D Day   4. 1940   5. The Channel Islands
6. The Battle of Britain   7. Barnes Wallis   8. 'Graf Spee'
9. (Benito) Mussolini   10. The Japanese attack on Pearl Harbour
11. World War I   12. He was a fighter pilot   13. Hiroshima and Nagasaki   14. The British invasion beaches in Normandy
15. Sarajevo   16. The Cross of Lorraine   17. General de Gaulle
18. Malta

Quiz No. 79   General Knowledge 27
1. A four-legged animal (literally, a four-footed animal)   2. Its back legs (hind)   3. Coventry   4. Seaweed   5. Sir Francis Drake
6. Your kneecap   7. Harvest   8. Christmas   9. 'Marching as to war'   10. Lent   11. Jerusalem   12. Easter   13. The Spanish Civil War   14. A (two-edged) sword; broadsword   15. *Macbeth*
16. Henry VIII   17. Cubit   18. Time flies

Quiz No. 80   Jobs
1. He drives sheep or cattle (usually to market)   2. Hats   3. He fells trees and saws them up   4. On high buildings   5. At the docks – he loads and unloads ships   6. He or she looks after a block of flats (or other buildings)   7. A pilot *or* aviator   8. A teacher, school-master
9. Printing   10. He shoes horses   11. A chiropodist   12. He makes and/or mends windows (works with glass)   13. Medicines, drugs
14. He makes or repairs clocks (or watches)   15. A cooper   16. A person who looked after horses; a stableman at an inn   17. Maps
18. He works in brass

Quiz No. 81   Rivers
1. The Seine   2. The Nile   3. The Shannon   4. The Thames (the Severn is also in Wales)   5. A tributary   6. Winding, flowing circuitously   7. Rome   8. The Mediterranean   9. The (south) Atlantic   10. The Zambezi   11. China   12. The St Lawrence
13. The Ganges   14. Australia   15. The Danube   16. Rhine
17. The Colorado   18. The Nile

Quiz No. 82   General Knowledge 28
1. The fox   2. Hands and nails   3. It is a miniature or dwarf tree, grown in a pot   4. Tickets   5. Thursday (after Thor)   6. Wood, pieces of wood   7. Plankton   8. Its trunk   9. A speech (or scene or

play) with only one actor   10. Borneo   11. Prison reform; care of prisoners   12. 0   13. Aries   14. The bull   15. As an archer 16. Scorpio   17. Virgin   18. By a pair of scales; a balance

Quiz No. 83   Legends
1. Red Riding Hood   2. By rubbing his lamp   3. The Pied Piper 4. William Tell   5. The Sheriff of Nottingham   6. Human blood 7. Rumpelstiltskin   8. Drake's   9. St Patrick   10. The Feast of Stephen   11. The devil (*literally* The Lord of the Flies)   12. The Holy Grail   13. The Unicorn   14. The centaur   15. A sword; King Arthur's sword   16. Merlin   17. Gawain   18. Damocles

Quiz No. 84   Nautical
1. 'The Victory'   2. Starboard   3. When a ship is about to set sail, or leave port   4. A pirate ship   5. 'The Titanic'   6. Joining them together   7. 'The Nautilus' (1955)   8. 'The Brittania'   9. She is sunk; holes are made in it (or opened) so it will sink   10. There is no disease aboard and it requires clearance   11. Its width (at the widest point)   12. Astern   13. Portsmouth   14. Sir Francis Chichester 15. 'HMS Bounty'   16. 'The Endeavour'   17. 'The Mayflower' 18. Tea

Quiz No. 85   General Knowledge 29
1. The Canaries   2. Sicily   3. South-east (east)   4. The Mediterranean   5. The Indian Ocean   6. Tasmania   7. A cat 8. An art gallery (a picture gallery, a collection of modern art)   9. White coffee (coffee with milk)   10. You disagree   11. Jewish, Hebrew 12. An invented language intended for international use   13. Bath 14. Ballet dancing   15. The brown wire   16. Muslims (Mohammedans)   17. George Bernard Shaw   18. (Anton) Chekhov

Quiz No. 86   London
1. Piccadilly Circus   2. Tower Bridge   3. The Tower of London 4. Trafalgar Square   5. Fish, fish market   6. Marble Arch (Hyde Park)   7. Berkeley Square   8. St Paul's Cathedral   9. Eastwards 10. The Old Bailey   11. Banking, finance   12. Baker Street 13. The Great Fire of London   14. The Trooping of the Colour 15. The House of Lords (Lord Chancellor's seat)   16. The Chancellor of the Exchequer   17. Westminster Abbey   18. A bus service (horse bus)

Quiz No. 87   Proverbs
1. Throw stones   2. 9   3. Straws   4. Deserves another 5. Is worth two in the bush   6. A long lane   7. A silk purse   8. A cat   9. He who laughs last   10. All work and no play   11. A watched pot   12. A bad workman   13. Parsnips   14. Necessity 15. Good intentions   16. An ill wind   17. Rome   18. Contempt

Quiz No. 88   General Knowledge 30
1. Toby   2. December 26th   3. A surgeon (doctor)   4. 5 5. Denmark (or Sweden or Norway)   6. Ultra high frequency 7. France   8. The tulip   9. The springbok   10. The eagle

11. Wales, China   12. We want to make peace   13. Red, Black, White, Yellow   14. Portugese   15. The Statue of Liberty   16. Venice   17. J. M. Barrie (James Barrie)   18. The African

Quiz No. 89   Mathematics
1. 1,000   2. 300   3. 20%   4. 0.75   5. 144   6. 6   7. 400   8. 60   9. An abacus   10. L   11. 100   12. 13   13. 4 score (80)   14. 78   15. A prime number   16. (plane) Geometry   17. quod erat demonstrandum   18. 2.2 lbs, 2¼ lbs

Quiz No. 90   Sport 3
1. 7   2. A piece of turf displaced by the player (when making a stroke)   3. Boxing   4. (Grand prix) motor racing   5. Muhammad Ali   6. South Africa   7. 15   8. Sailing/yachting   9. Shooting   10. Yachting/sailing   11. Rugby *Union* (England and Scotland)   12. 22 yards or 20.12 metres (chain)   13. Cricket   14. Tennis   15. Boxing   16. Gymnastics   17. Long jump or athletics   18. Cycling

Quiz No. 91   General Knowledge 31
1. 30   2. Your father   3. A bed   4. Batman   5. Venice (Amsterdam)   6. A mountain (the third highest mountain in the world)   7. The Indian Ocean   8. Hadrian's Wall   9. A scabbard   10. Bat   11. Cookery books   12. Edward VII   13. New York   14. Leningrad   15. Brussels   16. Stalingrad (also once called Tsaritsyn)   17. Florence   18. Rome

Quiz No. 92   Mountains
1. Ben Nevis   2. The Himalayas   3. France   4. South America   5. K2 (It is the 2nd highest mountain in the world)   6. Etna   7. Italy   8. New Zealand   9. Australia   10. Africa   11. The Pyrenees   12. Table Mountain   13. Mount Kilimanjaro   14. Mediterranean   15. Mexico   16. Ireland (Eire)   17. The Andes   18. Turkey

Quiz No. 93   Religion
1. Baptism (Christening)   2. The Lord's Prayer, 'Our Father'   3. Palm Sunday   4. Lent   5. The rosary   6. Its passion play (held every ten years)   7. A synagogue (temple)   8. Islam or Muslim   9. Buddhism   10. Hindu   11. Hebrew (Jewish)   12. Mecca (in Saudi Arabia)   13. Quakers   14. John Wesley   15. The Salvation Army   16. The Gideons   17. Mormons   18. Druids

Quiz No. 94   General Knowledge 32
1. Red, orange, yellow, green, blue, indigo, violet   2. Blue   3. Brown   4. Orange/yellow   5. Red   6. Blue   7. A mortar   8. A house   9. 4   10. Jupiter   11. Alexander Fleming   12. Pacific   13. Lover, seducer   14. *David Copperfield*   15. Denmark   16. Edward I   17. 1973   18. The sense of smell (noisome means evil-smelling)

Quiz No. 95   Paraphernalia
1. A (single) eye glass   2. For protection from the sun   3. To increase the sound of your voice, to help your voice to carry further   4. A kiln

5. A baton   6. Bounce along, jump up and down   7. Kneel on it
8. In paper (or banknotes, postage stamps)   9. Coke, charcoal or coal
10. Boring holes   11. A platform (for public speaking)   12. Across
your shoulder or the back of your neck   13. A mixture (originally of dried
flowers and spices)   14. On the back of a chair (to protect it from marks)
15. Sweep with it (it is a brush made from twigs)   16. A barrel or small
cask (*or* a measure of liquids)   17. A baby (it's a wicker cradle or pram)
18. A small basin

Quiz No. 96   British Royalty
1. King John   2. Boadicea   3. Robert (the Bruce)   4. Edward I
5. Canute   6. Alfred (of Wessex)   7. James I (1605)   8. Richard I
9. 2 (Anne Boleyn and Catherine Howard)   10. King John
11. Elizabeth I   12. George VI   13. George V   14. The Battle of
Hastings (Harold); The Battle of Bosworth (Richard III)   15. Victoria (63
years 7 months)   16. Prince Albert (of Saxe-Coburg-Gotha)
17. Henry VIII   18. Charles II

Quiz No. 97   General Knowledge 33
1. An aeroplane   2. Take a nap, a sleep (at midday)   3. A golfer
4. A St Bernard   5. Joseph   6. Other trees, especially apple trees
7. The Atlantic and Pacific   8. The Mediterranean and Atlantic Ocean
9. The Mediterranean and Gulf of Suez or Red Sea   10. The North Sea
and English Channel   11. The Bosphorous (or Bosporus)   12. The
Adriatic   13. Reykjavik   14. Commander Peary   15. Wasteful
(recklessly wasteful)   16. A diamond   17. (Dr Samuel) Johnson
18. A crown of laurel (or bay) leaves

Quiz No. 98   People
1. The countryside   2. Cockneys   3. Blind people   4. Ireland
(Eire) (Irish girl)   5. By rubbing noses   6. The Royal Canadian
Mounted Police   7. Witches   8. A monk or friar (it is a shaven patch
on the head)   9. Gold   10. Spain (south-west France)   11. New
Zealand   12. Mexico   13. A traitor; someone who co-operates with
the enemy   14. Bad news   15. Thief   16. Set fire to things   17.
A non-Jew (non-Mormon)   18. (South) Africa

Quiz No. 99   Popular Music
1. The Beatles   2. The Brotherhood of Man   3. World War I
4. Elvis Presley   5. Bill Haley (and the Comets)   6. 33 1/3
7. Wings   8. Cliff Richard   9. The Beatles   10. The Rolling
Stones   11. Abba   12. To pluck the strings of an instrument (zither,
guitar, etc.)   13. Bing Crosby   14. 'I'm Dreaming of a White
Christmas'   15. Louis Armstrong   16. The trumpet   17. Alan J.
Lerner, Frederick Loewe   18. Simon and Garfunkel

Quiz No. 100   General Knowledge 34
1. Circuses   2. Scotland (Ireland)   3. North America   4. An untrue
one; a made-up one   5. A spy story (a thriller)   6. Ulster, Northern
Ireland   7. One-tenth   8. Antirrhinum   9. Tea   10. The principal
singer in an opera; a leading lady   11. Pluto   12. Pontius Pilate
13. Pisces, Cancer, Scorpio   14. Leo, Aries, Sagittarius   15. Taurus,
Virgo, Capricorn   16. Pisces   17. Crab   18. Goat